living lighter
every day

LighterLife
Life in balance

living lighter
every day

First published in 2011 by LighterLife UK Limited

Recipes created by Bar Hewlett and Heather Thomas
LighterLife publication team: Bar Hewlett, Jackie Cox, Rebecca Hunter, Gill Mullins, Sue Dover and Lisa White

Designed and produced by SP Creative Design
Editor: Heather Thomas
Designer: Rolando Ugolini

Food photography: Simon Smith
Food stylist: Mari Meredid Williams

Acknowledgements
Image on pages 7 and 82: photography by Mark Cant; hair and makeup by Models1
Image on page 57: photography by Helen McArdle; hair and makeup by Models1

ISBN 978-0-9567073-0-7
Printed in Slovenia

contents

You and I are not what we eat; we are what we think.

Walter Anderson, 20th century American painter

Welcome...

...to a recipe book with a real difference – the LighterLife difference.

We're passionate about enabling people to enjoy a lighter life, including great food that's simple to cook, delicious to eat and helps you manage your weight into the bargain.

Sounds too good to be true, but it's not. When it comes to weight management, we're the experts. Since 1996 we've helped hundreds of thousands of people lose weight and keep it off with a simple philosophy that really works – change the way you think and you can change your life, including how you cook and eat, and how effectively you manage your weight.

So in this book you'll find food for thought as well as your table:
- How to encourage healthy thinking to help you make better food choices, including identifying when your hunger is emotional, not physical, and how to deal with it; and why 'comfort eating' is anything but.
- Easy, inspiring, flavour-filled recipes with no added fat, so you can enjoy great-tasting food without the excess calories. We've included savoury favourites for meat lovers and vegetarians alike, plus delicious desserts like peach and blueberry brûlée. You'll also find lots of hints and tips for healthy eating – from nutritional know-how to low-fat cooking techniques.

So, whether you're new to LighterLife or you've already achieved your weight-loss goals with us and are now enjoying your healthier, slimmer life, we hope you'll find this book a recipe for success both in and out of the kitchen.

The LighterLife Team

www.lighterlife.com

Claire dropped six dress sizes in six months with LighterLife (see pages 82–83 for her story).

7

Change your thinking, change your life

Healthy eating sounds so straightforward, but if it was then far more people would be doing it... At LighterLife we know that thinking in a more healthy, balanced way is the key to eating in a healthier way, too. It's all about creating a mindset for success – and that's what you can do with our expert tips, whch are featured over the next few pages.

Your goals for living lighter for life

Start making healthy eating and living choices by thinking about where you want to be and setting your goals for how to get there.

Set SMARTER goals for a healthy, lighter life:

Specific — State what you want to achieve and how you're going to do it.

Measurable — A goal that's easy to measure (like weight loss or weight management) is easy to keep track of.

Acceptable — You're more likely to achieve a goal that involves something you really want, and for you rather than for anyone else.

Realistic — Set yourself a realistic target.

Time-specific — Choose a time frame to keep you focused.

Exciting — If your goal fires you up, you'll be far keener to achieve it.

Recorded — Log your results so you can follow your progress – this can be very motivating, and it also enables you to spot any problem areas and work out what you can do to sort them out.

Recipe for success

- Break your goals into small, easily digestible chunks. A daily 'to do' list can be very useful.
- Write your goals down and review them regularly to make sure you're heading in the right direction.
- Check to see how the changes you're making are affecting your other needs and values, and the people in your life. If a particular goal seems increasingly and unhelpfully out of kilter with the reality of your life and your relationships, change it, or change the way you're trying to achieve it, to make it work for you.

Balanced thinking, balanced living

Do you 'find' yourself overeating and wonder how it happened? Do you 'find' yourself acting on an impulse to eat or drink so that before you realise it your hand's in the fridge and the food's in your mouth?

The key to dealing with this automatic behaviour is to bring the unhelpful, 'crooked' thoughts underlying these impulsive actions into your awareness, have a good look at them and decide whether they're going to bring you closer to your goals, or further away from them. If you realise you're about to do something that's not moving you towards your goals, or you notice a sudden, uncomfortable shift in mood, make a note of what's going on in your head – your thoughts, images, beliefs. This can help you identify what's happening, what will be a more helpful response, and then to act in a more helpful way.

The more you practise spotting these unhelpful thoughts – whether they're thoughts that affect your ability to manage your weight or anything else in your life – the easier it is to deal with them.

Recipe for success

Practise thinking in a more helpful way before you do something, especially when you're going into situations that you know may be challenging. Create a STOP sign in your mind:
Step back.
Think about what's going on.
Options: what choices do you have, what can you plan to do?
Proceed with your plan and notice how helpful it was.

CHECKLIST ✓

Ask yourself these balanced-thinking questions:
- What set this off – what was I doing?
- How do I feel?
- What thoughts or images ran through my head?
- What did I do when I started thinking like this?
- What's the evidence for and against these thoughts?
- What's a more helpful thought in this situation?
- What's the effect of this new way of thinking on my feelings and what can I do now?

Hunger: in your stomach or in your head?

There are two types of hunger – physical and emotional – and telling them apart is one of the keys to weight-management success.

As a tiny child, you're usually pretty in tune with your physical hunger, but as you grow up you may start to conform to what other people in your life want of you in terms of when you eat, how much and how often. This can lead to you losing touch with your physical hunger and with any real sense of when you're physically full.

If you believe that you're hungry for food when you're actually hungry for something else – such as affection, relaxation, a helping hand, some excitement in your life – this can lead to overeating.

Am I hungry?

When you have an urge to eat, check if it's emotional or physical hunger by taking time to ask yourself these 'am I hungry?' questions:
1   Have I got a hollow sensation in my stomach? Is it rumbling?
2   Am I thirsty?
3   Have I eaten anything in the last three or four hours?
4   Have I noticed a sudden change in my mood?

If you answer 'yes' to 3 and 4, it's more likely to be an emotional hunger than a physical one. Manage it by using your STOP technique or going through your balanced-thinking checklist (see page 9). Sometimes simply distracting yourself can be enough to interrupt it – try going for a walk, even if it's just round your house or workplace; have a glass of water or a hot drink; or just talk to or text a friend.

CHECKLIST ✓

If you decide you really *are* physically hungry, carefully plan what to eat:
● Hot or cold?
● Solid or liquid?
● Chewy, crunchy or soft?
● Savoury or sweet?
● A meal or a snack?
● With someone else or alone?

Now ask yourself the key question:
Will I be pleased with my food choice in two hours' time?

Recipe for success

You've probably caught yourself talking about 'comfort eating' – it's what people say they're doing when they're eating emotionally. Yet if you think about it it's actually 'discomfort eating' – eating to cover up a discomfort, to swallow down boredom, anger, fear, anxiety, sadness.

Recognising and dealing with your emotions openly, honestly and appropriately means they don't have to be covered up by food or drink in this way.

So if you catch yourself reaching for food 'for comfort', stop and think about what the real discomfort is, and how you can deal with it more effectively, without using food.

Managing you

Remember that your hand doesn't have a brain of its own, the fridge can't open on its own and food doesn't have a voice of its own. So, use your skills at challenging and changing your unhelpful, 'crooked' thoughts to give yourself more helpful choices.

This can be really useful for dealing with a lapse, where you do something that's not in line with your weight-management goals, like overeating in front of the television when you'd planned to go for a long walk with the dog then enjoy a healthy meal... Remember that a lapse is just a slip-up along the way. It wouldn't even be a lapse if you weren't committed to managing your weight effectively in the first place – it would just be a time that you ate.

Lapsing is actually a normal part of change, and it can be useful as it highlights situations, feelings and thoughts that are more likely to trigger overeating again if you don't address them. It's only when lapsing becomes persistent (relapse) that you're likely to be heading for long-term weight gain.

CHECKLIST ✓

If you think you're about to lapse:
- Go through your 'Am I hungry?' questions (see opposite).
- Ask yourself if eating or drinking is the only option you have in this situation.
- Ask yourself if regularly behaving like this is going to move you nearer to your goals.
- Imagine seeing yourself moving away from the food or drink and doing something completely different. Feel how satisfying that is.

Recipe for success

- A lot of what you do is habitual, and sometimes this can be unhelpful and prevent you from achieving your goals. Living a lighter life may mean making a lot of changes.
- So, start off by doing something different each day. It can be as simple as changing the way you sit or picking a new route to work. Each time you do something differently, your brain registers this as you changing.
- The more comfortable you become with changing how you do things – any things – then the easier change becomes to experience, and the more natural and acceptable the changes you're making to maintain a healthier weight will feel.

Healthy, lower-fat eating

At 9 kcal (kilocalories) per gram – more than twice as much as carbohydrate and protein – fat is the most energy-dense nutrient. Even in small amounts it adds a lot of energy (kilocalories) to your food, so keeping an eye on the fat in your eating plan is a practical way of managing your weight.

The most efficient way to do this is to cut out added fat – and in this book that's just what we've done. In a healthy, balanced diet you can get all the essential fats you need from meat, fish, nuts, seeds, grains and vegetables. You'll be amazed at how good food can taste without adding fat, and our virtually fat-free cooking techniques are easy to use, too. To help you create your own healthy eating plan, over the following pages we've included information on different foods, nutrients and healthy cooking techniques, and you'll find more at the start of each recipe section.

Your key food groups

Each food group has a vital role to play in a healthy diet, but everyone has different likes and dislikes, so if there's a particular food you'd rather avoid for any reason, just swap it for another in the same food group to ensure you're getting a good range of nutrients. The key is to find what works best for you, so experiment.

Carbohydrates

Carbs are your body's preferred source of energy. They include vegetables, fruit, bread, rice, pasta, noodles, oats and other breakfast cereals, maize, millet, cornmeal, plaintain, yams and green bananas. Unrefined carbohydrates – such as pulses (beans, peas and lentils), wholegrain cereals, brown rice, wholemeal bread and pasta, and starchy vegetables such as potatoes and sweet potatoes – retain most of their nutrients, including valuable B vitamins and dietary fibre. Sugar is a carbohydrate, but provides little in the way of other nutrients, and it causes tooth decay, too.

Dietary fibre

There are two types of dietary fibre. Insoluble fibre is found mainly in wholegrain breakfast cereals and breads, plus wheat bran and some fruit and vegetables, and can help keep your digestive system healthy, reducing your risk of constipation and other bowel problems. Soluble fibre is found in beans, porridge oats, barley, seeds, fruit and some vegetables, and may help to regulate cholesterol and blood-sugar levels.

Protein

Protein is important for cell growth and repair, and you also need it to make antibodies for a strong immune system. Sources include meat, fish, eggs, cheese, milk, yoghurt, nuts, seeds, pulses (peas, beans, lentils and peanuts), soya (including textured vegetable protein, tofu and tempeh), and mycoprotein (Quorn). Grains and cereals can also be a good source of protein for vegetarians.

Fats

Too much fat in your diet can be bad for your health and that's why we've chosen not to cook with any added fats in our recipes. Of course, as with any food group, it's not sensible to cut it out completely – and you'd find it tricky to do in any case, as fat is an essential component of so many foods. Even fruits and vegetables like raspberries and carrots contain tiny traces of fat*.

So why do you need fat? Well, it's a carrier for the fat-soluble vitamins A, D, E and K, and some types are 'essential', too. This means they're vital for good health, but can't be made in your body, so they have to come from your food instead. When it comes to managing your weight successfully, it pays to know your fats, to make sure you're topping up with the essential types and not wasting energy intake on the fats your body doesn't need or which can be actively harmful.

Unsaturated fats from plant foods play a healthy role in your eating plan. They include:
- **Monounsaturated fats**, which you'll find in nuts, seeds and avocados, as well as olive oil. Studies have found links between a 'Mediterranean'-style diet, which is rich in monounsaturated fats, and a reduced risk of heart disease and strokes.
- **Polyunsaturated fats,** which are divided into two main groups: omega 6 and omega 3. Omega 3 fats reduce your risk of heart disease, with oily fish the best source (see page 24) – if you're vegetarian, choose omega 3-rich plant foods instead, such as flaxseed, linseed or walnuts. Omega 6 fats are found in nuts, seeds, soya and whole grains, as well as vegetable oils, meat and dairy products, and can improve the ratio of 'good' HDL cholesterol to 'bad' LDL cholesterol, which reduces your risk of heart disease and strokes.

Saturated fat and trans fatty acids are the types of fat to really cut down on.
- **Saturated fat** comes mainly from animal sources such as butter, ghee, lard, suet and meat (although there are exceptions, such as palm and coconut oil). A diet high in saturated fats can raise your cholesterol levels and increase your risk of cardiovascular disease. So choose the leanest cuts of meat you can

and don't add saturates like butter, ghee or lard to your cooking – use our flavour-packed, no added fat recipes for inspiration.
- **Man-made trans fats** are found in some commercially processed foods, including cakes, biscuits, pastries, pies, ice cream and takeaways. They give food texture and prolong its shelf life – but they certainly won't prolong yours. They prevent your liver from processing fats properly, causing an imbalance in cholesterol levels and ratcheting up your risk of heart disease and stroke. There's no known safe level of consumption for man-made trans fats, and it's estimated that 11,000 heart attacks and 7,000 deaths each year in England alone could be prevented by just a one per cent reduction in intake[†]. Look on the label for '(partially) hydrogenated' fat or vegetable oil, 'vegetable shortening', 'margarine', and avoid like the plague.

Too much of a good thing...

The balance of omega 3 and omega 6 fats in your diet is important, too. Our hunter-gatherer ancestors' diets contained a maximum of four times the level of omega 6 to omega 3, whereas a modern diet can provide far too much omega 6 – up to 100 times more than your omega 3 intake. Too much omega 6 can be harmful, leading to a greater risk of blood clots and strokes, so keep your omega 3/6 levels in balance by cutting down on added vegetable oils and fried and processed foods, and bumping up your intake of nuts, seeds and oily fish.

*0.3g per 100g/3½oz
†British Medical Journal, 2010

Drinks

An effective way to reduce your energy intake is to change what you drink:

- Choose **water** – it's energy-free and kind to your teeth, too.
- Instead of regular, sugar-laden soft drinks, go for **diet versions**, which are kinder on your waistline and your teeth (although because many are acidic they might still increase your risk of tooth decay).
- In **tea and coffee**, use skimmed milk and cut down on sugar. Tea or coffee with whole milk and a teaspoon of sugar has over three times the calories of tea and coffee made with skimmed milk and no sugar. It might take you a little while to get used to, but you soon won't notice the change – except for the effect on your weight!
- **Go easy on the gourmet coffees**, as they often have a very high energy content, thanks to whole milk, cream, chocolate, caramel and flavoured syrups. A regular, sweetened gourmet coffee made with whole milk and flavoured syrup provides nearly as much energy as a standard (49g/2oz) bar of milk chocolate.
- At 7 kcal per gram, **alcohol** is almost as high in energy as fat, and the more you drink the more your inhibitions are lowered, so it's easy to end up eating and drinking excessively. Current UK recommendations are a maximum of two to three units a day for women and three to four units a day for men. It's a good idea to give your liver a rest by having a couple of alcohol-free days a week. Dilute spirits, wine and beer with low-cal or calorie-free mixers (mix white wine with soda to make a spritzer, or lager with low-cal lemonade for a shandy). And avoid crisps and salted nuts when drinking – they're high in energy, make you thirsty and encourage you to drink more, too.

Healthy, nutritious, delicious

Milk is a great source of calcium, protein, B vitamins and vitamins A and D. Skimmed milk contains just 0.1-0.3 per cent fat, compared to four per cent in whole milk and 1.7 per cent in semi-skimmed, and its calcium content is higher, too, making it the perfect choice for adults. (However, because it's so low in energy, and also because the skimming process removes virtually all of its vitamin A and D, it isn't suitable for children under five.)

Pure, 100% fruit or vegetable juices and fruit smoothies are packed with vitamins and minerals, and count towards your five a day for fruit and veg (see page 84). Swap a regular soft drink or gourmet coffee for fruit/vegetable juice, giving you more nutrients and fewer calories. But watch your intake: because smoothies and juices are high in fruit sugars, they'll still give you quite a lot of calories (on average 57 kcal/100ml for smoothies and 36 kcal/100ml for pure fruit juice) and their natural acidity can damage your teeth. Keep to one small glass, around 150ml (¼ pint), a day to enjoy the nutritional benefits without overdoing it on the calories.

Shopping healthily

Planning your meals and making a list can help you stay focused. Avoid food shopping on an empty stomach, as it's more likely to result in impulse buying. Think about how your purchases are moving you towards your weight-management goals, and go for these healthier buys:

- Fruit and veg: with canned varieties, choose fruit in natural juice and no added sugar, and vegetables or pulses in water with no added salt or sugar.
- Lean cuts of meat, reduced-fat mince (try turkey or Quorn), vegetarian burgers and sausages, fish canned in water or brine rather than oil.
- Reduced-fat milk and cheese, reduced fat/sugar yoghurts and fromage frais, and low-fat salad dressings.

Understanding food labels

Get into the habit of checking nutrition labels so you know exactly what you're buying. Labels that boast '75 per cent less fat' don't always tell the full story, because the item may still be very high in fat. Here's what to look for:

Ingredients on food labels are listed in descending order of weight, so if sugar is high up the list, the food is likely to contain lots.
Sugar: check for added sugars, including sucrose, glucose, fructose, maltose, honey, hydrolysed starch, invert sugar and corn syrup.
Fat: choose low-fat foods where possible – those with less than 3g fat (and less than 1.5g saturated fat) per 100g. High-fat foods have 20g or more of fat per 100g and are best limited.
Salt: this is often listed as sodium. Foods containing more than 1.5g salt (0.6g sodium) per 100g or more than 2.4g per portion are high in salt and best eaten only occasionally. Foods with 0.3g of salt or less (0.1g sodium or less) per 100g are low in salt. Salt = sodium x 2.5.

Traffic light labels

These focus on things it's important to limit for a healthy, balanced diet – sugars, fat, saturated fat and salt. Red means high levels of all these things; amber means medium levels; green means low levels. Generally, the more green lights on a traffic light label, the healthier the choice.

Guideline daily amount (GDA) labelling

GDAs are a guide to the amount of energy, fat, saturated fat, sugar and salt in the average adult's healthy diet. The GDA label shows at a glance the GDA contribution expressed as a percentage in a specified portion – but think about how realistic that portion size actually is. Are you really just going to eat the suggested tenth of that 'sharing' packet of crisps?

Healthy store cupboard

Keep well stocked with healthy basics, so you've always got the key ingredients for a balanced meal to hand:

- Frozen and tinned vegetables and pulses
- Dried lentils
- Tinned tomatoes, purée and passata
- Tinned, dried or frozen fruit
- Unsalted, non-roasted nuts and seeds
- Eggs
- Pasta, couscous, rice, noodles
- Frozen lean meat, poultry and fish
- Tofu
- Herbs and spices
- Vinegars
- Lemon juice
- Worcestershire sauce
- Low-fat stock or LighterLife Savoury Stock
- Soy sauce
- LighterLife ready meals – heat and serve pouches that are a convenient way of helping you maintain your weight.

Healthy cooking tips

Making some simple changes to the way in which you prepare and cook meals can help you achieve your goals for weight management and a healthier lifestyle.

Virtually fat-free cooking techniques
- Steam, poach, pressure cook, casserole, bake or roast without added fat, microwave, grill, barbecue or char-grill.
- Fish and seafood are good baked 'en papillote' (in a parcel of foil or greaseproof paper), which seals in flavour and prevents them drying out.
- Marinating adds flavour and tenderises, so food cooks more easily without added fat. Simply coat the food in the fat-free marinade, cover and refrigerate for a few hours prior to cooking.

How to fry in stock

Make a low-fat stock for sautéing by mixing half a teaspoon of LighterLife Savoury Stock with 100ml (3½fl oz) of boiling water.

Invest in some good-quality non-stick pans to prevent food from sticking when you're not adding fat (ideal for omelettes).

Cutting back on fat
- Go for low-fat options (see page 17).
- Always choose lean cuts of meat, including reduced-fat mince.
- Before cooking, trim visible fat from meat and remove the skin from poultry.
- Cook minced meat in water. When the meat has browned, and before you add the other ingredients, pour off the water and with it the fat released from the mince.
- Try naked, spread-free sandwiches, or use a little low-fat tomato salsa or purée, a low-fat dressing or a low-fat soft cheese such as quark instead.

Conserving vitamins
- Conserve vitamins in vegetables and fruit by steaming, pressure-cooking or microwaving rather than boiling.
- Serve when tender rather than over-soft.

Reducing salt
- Too much salt can raise your blood pressure and increase your risk of cardiovascular disease. Around three-quarters of the salt you eat comes already added to foods (including bread and breakfast cereals). Luckily, salt is something that taste buds adapt to, so cut down gradually over a few weeks and you'll get used to not adding salt.
- Put the salt cellar away when you cook and at the table, and instead boost the flavour of your food by marinating, cooking and dressing with herbs, spices, garlic, chilli, lemon or lime juice, vinegars, tomato purée, wine, capers, olives or mustard.
- Where possible, choose low-salt ingredients and foods (see page 17).

Tips for healthy eating

Get to know your food – go for whole foods: buy basic ingredients and reduce the amount of processed food you buy, so you know exactly what's going into your meals. Read the labels thoroughly – check what's in there, using our guide on page 17. Cut right back on saturated fat, sugar and salt, and don't add fat – you can see from our delicious recipes that it's simply not necessary.

Have plenty of vegetables and fruit – at least five portions a day (page 84). Vegetables and fruits are often at their best in season, and cheaper too. Think like a rainbow – go for lots of different colours to get a really wide range of nutrients and add interest and excitement.

Balance your intake throughout the day to help keep your blood-sugar levels steady, preventing hunger pangs and mood swings which might otherwise lead to overeating. Eating fibre-rich foods can help, including pulses, vegetables, fruit, wholegrains and wholemeal products.

Stay well hydrated – drinking water is a great, calorie-free way to do this.

Eat fish a couple of times a week, including a serving of oily fish like salmon, or keep up your omega 3 intake with seeds and nuts if you're vegetarian.

Create your own healthy eating plan – for successful weight-management there's no one-size-fits all approach. For example, you might find it helpful to eat more veg and less fruit, or to stick simply to three meals a day, or to have six small meals instead, or to try different foods within your key food groups so you eat more pulses and less bread... The key is to experiment to find an enjoyable plan that works best for unique you.

Enjoy your food – and our recipes!

Your recipe for success

Set goals Celebrate your successes and plan for your future achievements by setting goals for your weight and your life. Create a 'film clip' in your head of what this looks like, and play it back when you need a boost.

Balance your thinking Stop, identify and interrupt any unhelpful thinking habits that can throw you off track.

Balance your eating Create a healthy, balanced eating plan that works for you.

Give yourself boundaries Set yourself firm guidelines, like a weight above which you don't want to go, or a pair of trousers with a tight waistband. Then take action: moving more, rebalancing your food intake or, preferably, both!

Use a food and mood diary This helps you identify what you're doing that works, as well as the times you might use food in unhelpful ways.

Keep it up Don't let a momentary lapse become an unhelpful habit. Recommit to your goals and start again.

Recognise your achievements Write down what's gone well for you every day to focus on your success and your goals.

Enjoy a more active lifestyle Being more active is great for your health – both body and mind – and it's great for managing your weight, too. Everything counts. Use your imagination!

success story

Varsha

dropped five dress sizes in five months

" When a friend decided to go to a LighterLife information session, I volunteered to go with her for moral support. What I learnt there was so inspiring that I decided to sign up.

I needed to change my eating completely. Growing up, I was one of three children from an Asian family and my father was quite strict about us finishing everything on our plates. Then, as an adult, I always had big portions and seconds if I felt like it. When Harish and I got married in 2001 we both piled on weight. We were in a comfort zone – going out lots and eating things like kebabs and pizza. We're both vegetarians but it didn't mean we were any slimmer! Our favourite home-cooked dishes were potato curries, pasta dishes with spicy, creamy sauces; and lots of naan bread. We didn't have much energy and often felt bloated and irritable with each other.

What LighterLife gave me was the opportunity to evaluate my eating habits properly, and with very clear boundaries. Harish saw me losing weight quickly and was impressed. He followed my example and started LighterLife, too.

When I reached my weight-loss goal, I was apprehensive about reintroducing conventional food, but as it's week by week I adapted fairly easily and found LighterLife's structured approach very helpful.

Now, I'm managing my weight successfully, I still enjoy cooking but the fat and sugar content is much lower. For instance, I often make chilli paneer, which involves stir-frying paneer (cheese) cubes and then adding vegetables and tomato purée for a kind of light stew. It's really simple and all the family love it – including our children. *"*

Varsha
Dress size then: 22
Dress size now:12

Harish
Waist size then: 40in
Waist size now: 32in

Harish

lost eight inches from his waist in four months

"For several years my wife and I had tried so many diets and just given up because we couldn't stick to them.

I'd come to the conclusion that I simply couldn't change. Then, in June 2009, Varsha told me that she was starting LighterLife Total. I shrugged it off as another one of those moments where she'd sign up for something and then give up after a week or so.

Within a month of Varsha's success on Total I could see a major difference in her appearance and was really impressed she hadn't quit. As she slimmed down, friends would make jokes at my expense, asking if I was eating my wife! That's when it really hit home that I needed to do something about my weight.

I started LighterLife for Men in September 2009. In my men's group, I could discuss issues and share feelings that guys wouldn't normally discuss. The hardest part of the programme was getting through Diwali, Christmas and New Year's Day, which all involve lots of food and drink. Having stuck by the programme it made me realise I could still enjoy myself without piling on weight. Food had just been a crutch.

Nowadays, my wife and I cook a lot more stir-fries and experiment with more exotic vegetables. We still eat out but we use the knowledge we gained from our meetings to make healthier choices.*"*

www.lighterlife.com

Harish, now a 32in waist

Varsha, now a size 12

savoury

fish

Quick to prepare, light to eat and bursting with flavour and nutrients, fish is always a wonderful meal.

Compared to even just a few years ago, you'll find far more fish choices on the high street, from the farmed and exotic to the humble British line-caught mackerel. Fish is best eaten as fresh as possible and cooked gently, to prevent the delicate, moist flesh from drying out. Firm flesh and bright eyes are good indicators of freshness, while sunken, cloudy-eyed fish with flabby flesh, or those that smell 'fishy' are best avoided.

Oily fish includes anchovies, herring, mackerel, pilchards, salmon, sardines and trout (fresh tuna is an oily fish, but the canning process removes most of the natural oils, so canned is classed as a white fish). It's a good source of vitamins A and D, and oily fish contains the type of omega 3 fatty acids known as 'long-chain' fatty acids – EPA (eicosapentaenoic acid) and DHA (docosahexaenoic acid) – which can reduce your risk of heart disease. Your body can make these fatty acids from other foods, but not very efficiently, so getting them directly from oily fish is a better option.

24

White fish, such as cod, coley, haddock, monkfish, plaice, pollack, sea bass, sea bream, sole and turbot, is very low in fat (less than five per cent) and calories. It does contain omega 3 fatty acids, but in far lower concentrations than oily fish.

Shellfish are low in fat and a good source of minerals like selenium, zinc, iodine and copper. They include cockles, crayfish, langoustine, lobster, prawns, scallops, shrimps and whelks. Other types, including crab, mussels, oysters and squid, are also rich in omega 3 fatty acids.

To make the most of fish's health benefits, eat two portions a week, including one of oily fish and omega 3-rich shellfish – and with terrific recipes like walnut and anchovy crusted salmon, tandoori-spiced fish, and crab and couscous summer salad, that will be easy!

Note: For more information on oily and white fish, visit www.eatwell.gov.uk

Cholesterol in shellfish

While crustacean shellfish (crab, lobster, prawns, squid and octopus) contain dietary cholesterol, for most people this has little effect on their blood cholesterol levels – saturated fat intake plays a far larger role in raising these. So, unless you've been advised otherwise by your GP, you can enjoy shellfish as part of your healthy, balanced diet.

Tangy smoked mackerel pâté

Preparation: 5 minutes
Serves: 2
Per serving:
282 kcal
17g protein
13g carbs
18g fat

115g (4oz) smoked mackerel fillet (approximately 1 medium fillet)
60g (2oz) quark or virtually fat-free fromage frais
½ teaspoon balsamic vinegar
½ teaspoon Worcestershire sauce
freshly ground black pepper
1 tablespoon snipped chives
mixed salad leaves or toasted bread, to serve
lemon wedges, to garnish

This could be the easiest light meal you're ever likely to make, but it's also one of the most delicious and so quick to put together that it makes a great lunch if you're in a hurry. Serve it simply with a crisp salad or, if you want to make this pâté more substantial, spread it on a slice of nutty, whole-grain bread and garnish with some cherry tomatoes.

1 Carefully remove any bones from the smoked mackerel fillet, and discard the skin.

2 Put the smoked mackerel in a food processor or blender with the quark or fromage frais, balsamic vinegar and Worcestershire sauce. Add a grinding of black pepper – just enough to taste.

3 Blitz briefly until all the ingredients are combined to a smooth mixture. If you don't have a food processor or blender, just mix in a pestle and mortar, although the pâté may have a rougher texture.

4 Mix in the chives and then press the smoked mackerel mixture into a small dish or two individual ramekins, then cover with cling film and chill in the refrigerator until required.

5 Serve the pâté with some mixed salad leaves or spread it on toast, garnished with lemon wedges.

Tips

- This recipe is incredibly quick to make but if you're really short on time you can easily buy boneless smoked mackerel fillets, which will save you having to fish out all the little bones.
- If you've bought a packet of smoked mackerel you can use up any remaining fillets the next day in a delicious salad. Have a look at the salad dressing recipes on page 139 for some ideas.

Or...

For a special occasion, make a smoked salmon pâté in the same way. Use smoked salmon trimmings, which are cheaper than slices, and blitz them in a blender with quark. Flavour with lemon juice, black pepper and some chopped fresh dill. Delicious!

French tuna salad

Preparation: 10 minutes
Cooking: 10 minutes
Serves: 2
Per serving:
298 kcal
36g protein
34g carbs
2g fat

1 red pepper, cut in half lengthways
and deseeded

175g (6oz) French beans, trimmed
and cut in half

1 x 185g (6½oz) can tuna in brine,
drained

1 x 400g (14oz) can butter beans,
drained and rinsed

2 spring onions, chopped

a few drops of balsamic vinegar

2 tablespoons coarsely chopped
fresh coriander

freshly ground black pepper

This recipe is a healthy variation on a classic salade niçoise from southern France. It makes a very easy light lunch or you can serve it with crisp lettuce and ripe tomatoes for a more substantial supper dish.

1 Preheat the grill to medium and then place the red pepper, skin-side up, on the grill pan. Grill for about 5 minutes, until the skin blisters and blackens.

2 Remove the pepper from the heat and leave to cool in a covered container or a sealed plastic bag. The trapped steam will enable you to remove the skin more easily.

3 Meanwhile, steam the French beans for 4–5 minutes. They should be tender but still have some bite. Immerse the beans immediately in a bowl of cold water to stop the cooking process and help retain their vibrant colour. Drain thoroughly.

4 When the red pepper pieces are cool enough to handle, remove the charred skin, ribs and seeds, and chop the flesh into small chunks.

5 In a large bowl, mix together the chunks of tuna with the red pepper, French beans, butter beans and spring onions.

6 Sprinkle with a few drops of balsamic vinegar and the coriander. Add a good grinding of black pepper and serve immediately.

Tip

If you don't have any butter beans in the store cupboard, don't despair. Red kidney beans or speckled borlotti beans will taste just as good and add more colour. You can even make it with a mixture of canned beans, including haricots and flageolets, for a really pretty dish.

Or...

Add two quartered medium-sized, hard-boiled eggs to make a more filling meal. This will add 73 kcal, 7g protein and 5g fat per portion.

Crab and couscous summer salad

Preparation: 15 minutes
Standing: 10 minutes
Serves: 2
Per serving:
315 kcal
31g protein
32g carbs
7g fat

75g (2½oz) couscous
150ml (¼ pint) boiling water
juice of ½ lemon
2 tablespoons balsamic vinegar
1 tablespoon quark or virtually fat-free fromage frais
225g (8 oz) crab meat, flaked (or crab sticks)
4 spring onions, trimmed and finely chopped
¼ red onion, finely chopped
175g (6oz) ripe cherry tomatoes, quartered
¼ cucumber, diced
freshly ground black pepper
4 tablespoons chopped fresh mint
mixed salad leaves, to serve
lemon wedges, to garnish

The beauty of this salad is that it can be prepared in advance and then chilled in the fridge for a few hours until you're ready to eat. You could even take an individual portion (sealed in an airtight container) to work with you as a packed lunch. If you can't get hold of fresh or frozen crab, use canned instead.

1 Put the couscous in a large bowl and pour over the boiling water. Cover the bowl with cling film or a plate and leave to stand for about 10 minutes, or until all of the water has been absorbed.

2 In another bowl, whisk together the lemon juice, balsamic vinegar and quark or fromage frais until thoroughly blended.

3 Gently stir in the crab meat, spring onions, red onion, cherry tomatoes and cucumber, and mix well to combine.

4 Finally, fluff the couscous, separating the grains with a fork, and add this to the crab mixture, stirring well. Season with black pepper to taste and gently mix in the chopped mint.

5 Cover the couscous salad and chill in the fridge until required. Serve on a bed of salad leaves, garnished with a wedge of lemon.

Tip

An alternative way to serve this lovely salad is to top each portion with a spoonful of virtually fat-free fromage frais. You can even fold a little into the couscous before serving for a different texture.

Or...

- Make a traditional vegetarian Lebanese tabbouleh with bulgur wheat instead of couscous. Soak in the same way, leaving it to stand for about 15 minutes before stirring in the chopped vegetables and herbs. To make it more colourful, add some chopped, grilled sweet red and yellow peppers and torn coriander leaves or flat-leaf parsley. Omit the fromage frais (or quark) and sprinkle with some lemon juice and balsamic vinegar before serving.
- If you love hot, spicy food, serve the couscous with some authentic harissa paste or a spoonful of Thai sweet red chilli sauce.

Walnut and anchovy crusted salmon

Preparation: 10 minutes
Cooking: 15 minutes
Serves: 2
Per serving:
466 kcal
41g protein
8g carbs
30g fat

2 x 150g (5oz) salmon fillets, skin removed

freshly ground black pepper

finely grated zest and juice of ½ small lemon

30g (1oz) stale white breadcrumbs

30g (1oz) walnut pieces, roughly chopped

a small handful of parsley, woody stalks removed, then chopped

1 anchovy fillet, drained and finely chopped

assorted steamed vegetables, e.g. asparagus, baby carrots, thin green beans, mangetout

lemon wedges, to garnish

If you can find them, try to buy wild salmon fillets in preference to the farmed ones – they taste much better, especially the Alaskan ones. Oily fish are an excellent source of protein and are high in omega 3 fatty acids, which are essential for your health, so try to include them in your diet at least once a week.

1 Preheat the oven to 180°C, gas mark 4.

2 Arrange the salmon fillets on a non-stick baking tray and season them lightly with freshly ground black pepper.

3 In a small bowl, mix together the lemon zest and juice, breadcrumbs, walnuts, parsley and chopped anchovy. Spoon this mixture over each salmon fillet, pressing down lightly to cover it.

4 Bake in the preheated oven for approximately 15 minutes, until the fish is cooked and the topping is crisp and golden brown.

5 Carefully transfer the salmon fillets to two warm serving plates and serve immediately with a selection of steamed vegetables and a wedge of lemon to garnish.

Tip

You can buy breadcrumbs in most supermarkets but here's what to do if you can't get hold of them or want to make your own. This recipe works best with slightly stale bread. Preheat the oven to 150°C, gas mark 2, and then pop one slice of medium-sliced white bread directly onto the oven shelf and leave for 5 minutes. When the bread is crisp on the outside but still white inside it's ready. Remove the crusts and blitz in a food processor or blender for 30 seconds. Don't worry if you don't have a white loaf as wholemeal bread works just as well.

Or...

● This works equally well with other oily fish, including fresh tuna.
● If you don't want to use breadcrumbs, this tastes equally delicious without them – or you can substitute rolled oats.

Salmon, pea and broccoli pasta

Preparation: 10 minutes
Cooking: 10 minutes
Serves: 2
Per serving:
399 kcal
34g protein
32g carbs
15g fat

1 shallot, thinly sliced
200ml (7fl oz) vegetable stock **or** LighterLife Savoury Stock
100g (3½oz) tagliatelle
85g (3oz) frozen peas
85g (3oz) broccoli florets, roughly chopped
200g (7oz) salmon fillet, skinned and cut into large cubes
1 tablespoon capers
grated zest of ½ lemon
2 tablespooons virtually fat-free fromage frais
freshly ground black pepper
2 tablespoons snipped chives

Pasta fills you up and makes a quick and easy supper dish when you get home from work and don't have much time to cook. This recipe takes no longer to prepare and cook than heating up a ready meal – and it tastes much better! Don't worry if you don't have any tagliatelle in the cupboard; you can use fettuccine or even spaghetti or linguine instead.

1 Put the sliced shallot in a saucepan and cook gently in a little of the stock for about 5 minutes, until softened.

2 Meanwhile, bring a large saucepan of water to the boil and then add the tagliatelle. Cook over a high heat for about 8 minutes (according to the packet instructions) until the pasta is just tender but still retains some bite (al dente).

3 While the pasta is cooking, add the peas, broccoli and salmon to the shallots and pour in the remaining stock. Cover the pan and cook gently for 5 minutes, until the fish is cooked and opaque, the vegetables are tender and most of the stock has been absorbed.

4 When the pasta is cooked, drain well and then return it to the hot pan. Gently stir in the capers and lemon zest and, lastly, the fromage frais. Season to taste with freshly ground black pepper.

5 Divide the hot pasta between two serving plates and then top with the drained pea, broccoli and salmon mixture. Sprinkle with snipped chives and serve immediately.

Tips

● When cooking pasta, always use a large saucepan and bring the water to a rolling boil before adding the pasta. Boil for the specified time until it's cooked but still firm enough to give a little resistance when you bite into it. This is called al dente (literally 'to the tooth').
● Take care when stirring in the fromage frais. Do it off the heat and mix through very gently to prevent it curdling. Serve immediately.

Or...

If you're in a real hurry, just stir 85g (3oz) chopped smoked salmon or 115g (4oz) cooked peeled prawns, plus the capers, lemon zest and fromage frais, into the pan of cooked, drained pasta. Toss lightly, grind over some black pepper, and serve at once, sprinkled with chopped dill.

Tandoori spiced fish

Preparation: 10 minutes
Cooking: 15–20 minutes
Serves 2
Per serving:
203 kcal
37g protein
7g carbs
3g fat

85g (3oz) low-fat natural yoghurt
¼ teaspoon ground turmeric
2 teaspoons tandoori curry paste
2 x 150g (5oz) skinned white
fish fillets
freshly ground black pepper
lime wedges, to garnish
plain boiled basmati rice, to serve
spinach or green beans, to serve

Cucumber raita
½ cucumber
5 tablespoons low-fat natural
yoghurt
2 tablespoons chopped mint
1 tablespoon chopped coriander
squeeze of lime juice
seeds of ½ pomegranate (optional)
freshly ground black pepper

Any firm white fish fillets can be used in this recipe, especially cod, haddock, halibut and monkfish. You can buy ready-made tandoori curry paste in most supermarkets as well as specialist delicatessens.

1 Preheat the oven to 190°C, gas mark 5.

2 Make the cucumber raita: use a potato peeler to cut the cucumber into long strips lengthways. Mix in a bowl with the yoghurt, herbs, lime juice and pomegranate seeds (if using). Season with black pepper, then cover and chill in the refrigerator until you're ready to serve.

3 In a shallow dish, mix together the yoghurt, turmeric and tandoori curry paste. Place the fish fillets in this spicy mixture, coating them on both sides. Sprinkle with black pepper and then place them in a shallow ovenproof dish. Cover with kitchen foil.

4 Bake in the preheated oven for 10 minutes, then remove the foil covering and cook for a further 5–10 minutes, until the fish is cooked through and slightly browned.

5 Serve the spiced fish immediately, garnished with lime wedges, with the cucumber raita, plain boiled basmati rice and steamed spinach or green beans.

Tips
- Check the fish fillets for small bones before coating them in the spicy yoghurt mixture.
- If you don't have a lime, don't worry – just use a lemon instead.

Or...
Use the same tandoori yoghurt marinade for coating skinned chicken breasts. Score them two or three times with a knife first and rub the yoghurt mixture all over, paying particular attention to the scored areas. Bake in the oven in the same way for 20–25 minutes, until the chicken is thoroughly cooked through.

Oriental scallops with noodles

Preparation: 10 minutes
Cooking: 15 minutes
Serves: 2
Per serving:
237 kcal
30g protein
22g carbs
3g fat

100g (3½oz) rice noodles

4 tablespoons vegetable stock **or** LighterLife Savoury Stock

1 small onion, finely chopped

2 garlic cloves, crushed

2 tablespoons finely chopped fresh root ginger

225g (8oz) scallops

1 red pepper, deseeded and cut into strips

85g (3oz) mangetout

3 spring onions, sliced

2 teaspoons soy sauce

freshly ground black pepper

1 Thai bird's eye chilli, cut into thin slivers

coriander leaves, to garnish

Fresh scallops are quite expensive and are not always readily available, but the frozen ones taste equally delicious in this recipe and you can buy them in most supermarkets. If using, always thaw them thoroughly before cooking. Scallops are highly nutritious – they are a great source of lean protein and very low in fat.

1 Soak and cook the rice noodles according to the instructions on the packet, and drain well.

2 While the noodles are cooking, put the stock in a large, heavy-based frying pan or wok. Add the onion, garlic and ginger and cook quickly, stirring, until softened and golden.

3 Add the scallops and cook for 2 minutes each side. Don't overcook or they will become quite tough – they should be juicy and succulent. Remove the scallops and place them in a covered dish to keep warm.

4 Add the red pepper, mangetout and spring onions to the pan, together with the soy sauce, and stir-fry briskly for 3–4 minutes, until the mangetout are bright green and starting to get tender.

5 Gently fold in the cooked rice noodles and scallops and heat through for 1 minute. Season with black pepper to taste.

6 Divide the mixture between two serving plates, and garnish with slivers of chilli and fresh coriander leaves. Serve immediately.

Tip

You don't need oil to stir-fry authentic-tasting Chinese and Thai dishes. Just cook the vegetables briefly in a little stock, and keep stirring and moistening them, as necessary, with stock, soy sauce or Thai fish sauce for an oriental flavour.

Or...

- Use raw shelled tiger prawns instead of scallops. They will add even more colour to this dish and taste great.
- Add some strips of carrot, broccoli florets, pak choi or shredded spring greens, depending on what is available.

success story

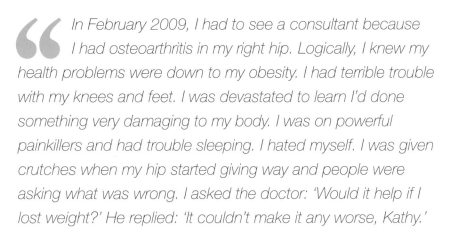

Kathy

dropped eight dress sizes in nine months

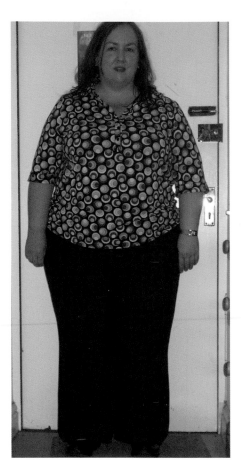

Kathy
Dress size then: 24
Dress size now: 8

" *In February 2009, I had to see a consultant because I had osteoarthritis in my right hip. Logically, I knew my health problems were down to my obesity. I had terrible trouble with my knees and feet. I was devastated to learn I'd done something very damaging to my body. I was on powerful painkillers and had trouble sleeping. I hated myself. I was given crutches when my hip started giving way and people were asking what was wrong. I asked the doctor: 'Would it help if I lost weight?' He replied: 'It couldn't make it any worse, Kathy.'*

I asked if he could delay the operation on my hip so I could lose some weight. I'd seen an advert for LighterLife and I wanted to give it a go. To his credit, he agreed. Within a year of my weight loss, I was told that I no longer needed the operation – my joints were recovering.

Looking back, it's not hard to see why I put on so much weight over the years. I ate lots of pre-packaged meals, which were quite nutritious but drowning in calories. I particularly loved salmon and steak covered in breadcrumbs. My other favourite meals were stuffed mushrooms with lots of cheese on top, stuffed baked potatoes, and crisps with sour cream dips. I'd eat double portions and then feel really guilty, which would lead to my eating even more!

LighterLife has completely transformed my life. Being on Total gave me enough time to break my unhealthy habits. Initially, when I went back to conventional food I was worried I'd overeat again but, incredibly, I found my palate had changed.

I don't crave sugar, salt and carbs any more.
I prefer fresh, healthy food. Also, for someone
who could barely be bothered to eat an apple
in the past, I really love fruit of all kinds now.

These days, everything I buy is in its raw form.
For instance, if I want shepherd's pie I'll buy
fresh minced meat and potatoes and prepare
it myself. Nothing is processed or packaged.
Even packaged salads are often full of salt
and fattening dressings, so it pays to be careful.
I love lamb, trout and salmon, which I dry-fry
in a special griddle pan – it takes less then
10 minutes. I cook my vegetables in a steamer.
I also take packed lunches to work. I might put
prawns and avocado salad in a tortilla wrap with
a little balsamic vinegar – it's delicious.

Losing weight on LighterLife has given me the
motivation to keep the weight off permanently.
I've learnt so much about myself, too. The group
work taught me that I used food to isolate myself
from the world and to cope with stress, shyness
and anxiety. Now my confidence is increasing.

I have a saying on my fridge that reads:
'If hunger is not the problem, then eating is
not the solution.' I agree wholeheartedly
with that philosophy, and this
encapsulates LighterLife for me. "

**Kathy, now
a size 8**

www.lighterlife.com

chicken

> " *I will see to it that no peasant in my kingdom will lack the means to have a chicken in the pot every Sunday.* "
>
> *Henri IV of France*

Tender, versatile, low in fat and great value for money, chicken is a real family favourite.

Once regarded as a luxury, chicken is now probably the world's most popular meat, not least because it cooks so easily and beautifully by almost any method you can think of – from roasting to baking, sautéing to grilling, poaching to casseroling.

It's also a really healthy choice – skinless chicken is low in fat compared with red meats, typically providing just 2g of fat and 150 kcal per 100g. While the white breast meat is slightly lower in energy and fat than the darker leg meat, the legs are slightly richer in iron, zinc and B vitamins – so you can enjoy great nutritional benefits eating whichever you like best.

A whole chicken can often be far better value than buying individual cuts, such as breast or thigh, giving you enough meat for a (low-fat) roast plus plenty left over for using up in salads and pasta dishes.

Our recipes include new twists on old favourites, such as olive-baked chicken and chicken ratatouille, and they're all designed to be as low in fat as possible, so you can enjoy the taste without the waist.

Handling chicken safely

- When preparing chicken, use a separate chopping board and knife, and wash them thoroughly in warm, soapy water afterwards.
- Don't rinse chicken prior to cooking, as this will simply spread any bacteria it contains over a wider area. Thorough cooking will kill off any germs, so make sure that the chicken is cooked until the juices run clear with no traces of blood (always test with a skewer, particularly the area of breast closest to the leg).
- If you're using frozen chicken, remove it from its packaging and either defrost in the fridge or microwave in a deep dish to catch any of the liquid that comes out. You should allow 24 hours in the fridge for a 900g (2lb) chicken and 36 hours for a 1.8kg (4lb) bird.

Curried chicken salad

Preparation: 10 minutes
Serves: 2
Per serving:
320 kcal
38g protein
33g carbs
4g fat

60g (2oz) dried apricots

5 tablespoons quark or virtually fat-free fromage frais

2 teaspoons curry paste

1 tablespoon mango chutney

30g (1oz) raisins

1 small apple, cored and cut into small chunks

3 spring onions, thinly sliced

2 x 100g (3½oz) cooked chicken breasts **or** 200g (7oz) cooked leftover chicken, cut into bite-sized chunks

freshly ground black pepper

1 x 90g (3oz) bag of mixed salad leaves

plain, boiled basmati rice, to serve (optional)

This salad is basically a classic coronation chicken recipe without all the calories, and it's absolutely delicious. If you have a low-fat roast chicken dinner planned, then this recipe is a fantastic way of using up the leftovers as well as being a great mid-week supper as it's so quick to put together.

1 Place the apricots in a small bowl and pour 3 tablespoons of boiling water over them. Set aside to soften for at least 5 minutes and then drain well. Chop them into small pieces.

2 In a large bowl, mix the quark or fromage frais with the curry paste and mango chutney. Add the raisins, apricots, apple and half of the sliced spring onions. Mix thoroughly to combine and then add the chunks of cooked chicken. Stir again, season to taste with black pepper, and then cover and chill in the fridge until needed.

3 To serve the salad, arrange the salad leaves on two serving plates and spoon the chicken mixture over the top. Garnish with the remaining spring onions and serve immediately. If wished, you can serve it with plain boiled or flavoured basmati rice (see below).

Tip

This recipe also works brilliantly with leftover turkey instead of chicken. In fact, it's a welcome change on Boxing Day when you fancy eating something simple, light and easy.

Or...

- If you're serving this salad as a more substantial meal with boiled rice (as shown opposite), you can flavour and colour it with chopped herbs, spring onions, green beans, saffron strands, cardamom pods or even ruby-red pomegranate seeds.
- Vegetarians can substitute Quorn pieces for the chicken in this salad.

Chicken and goat's cheese salad with raspberry dressing

Preparation: 10 minutes
Cooking: 15 minutes
Serves: 2
Per serving:
485 kcal
53g protein
21g carbs
21g fat

2 x 150g (5oz) cooked, skinless chicken breasts
1 tablespoon raspberry vinegar
2 tablespoons quark or virtually fat-free fromage frais
freshly ground black pepper
1 bag mixed salad leaves, e.g. watercress, rocket, baby spinach leaves
30g (1oz) pine nuts
115g (4oz) fresh raspberries
60g (2oz) goat's cheese
crusty bread, to serve (optional)

This lovely summer salad is really quick and easy to make and looks fabulous. Some goat's cheeses are more creamy than others, and if you buy one that is not too crumbly, you could cut it into 30g (1oz) slices and grill them instead until they are appetizingly golden brown and just starting to melt.

1 With a sharp knife, cut each each chicken breast into thin slices lengthways. Set aside.

2 Make a dressing by whisking together the raspberry vinegar and quark or fromage frais. Season to taste with black pepper.

3 Divide the salad leaves between two serving plates and arrange the sliced chicken on top. Scatter with pine nuts and raspberries and then crumble over the goat's cheese. Drizzle the dressing over the salad.

4 Serve the chicken salad immediately – with some crusty fresh bread or sliced baguette, if wished.

Tips

- You can buy raspberry vinegar in most supermarkets and specialist delicatessens. You don't need to use much to get the benefits of its wonderful flavour, and a little goes a long way. It helps to transform an ordinary salad into something special.
- The salad will look even prettier if you briefly roast the pine nuts until golden in a medium oven.

Or...

- In winter, when raspberries are out of season and are difficult to find or very expensive, use bitter winter leaves in the salad, such as chicory and radicchio, and serve the chicken in its dressing with goat's cheese, sliced juicy pear and chopped walnuts.
- If you're vegetarian, you can use Quorn fillets instead of chicken.

One-pot chicken with rice and peas

Preparation: 5 minutes
Cooking: 40 minutes
Serves: 2
Per serving:
365 kcal
39g protein
32g carbs
9g fat

2 shallots, diced

250ml (8fl oz) chicken stock or LighterLife Savoury Stock

100g (3½oz) risotto rice, e.g. Arborio

100g (3½oz) frozen peas,

200g (7oz) cooked chicken, shredded

grated zest of ½ lemon

freshly ground black pepper

a small handful of basil leaves, roughly chopped

lemon wedges, to garnish

cherry tomatoes on the vine

This tasty chicken dish is fantastic because it's really simple to make and everything cooks in the same pot, so there's hardly any washing-up to do afterwards. It's the perfect meal at the end of a busy day.

1 Cook the shallots in a little of the stock in a heavy-based saucepan over a low heat, until softened and golden – approximately 5 minutes. Add the risotto rice and stir for 1 minute.

2 Pour in the rest of the stock, then cover the saucepan and bring to a gentle simmer. Cook for approximately 25 minutes, or until the rice is cooked and just tender.

3 Stir in the frozen peas, about three-quarters of the chicken and half the grated lemon zest. Season to taste with freshly ground black pepper and continue cooking gently for 5 minutes.

4 To serve, divide the rice mixture between two serving plates and top with the remaining chicken and lemon zest. Sprinkle the chopped basil over each portion and serve with a wedge of lemon and some raw, grilled or roasted cherry tomatoes on the vine.

Tip

You can use an onion instead of shallots in this recipe, although it won't be so mild. For a more intense flavour, try cooking the shallots with some crushed garlic or sliced leeks.

Or...

- If you have some leftover cooked turkey, you can substitute this for the chicken. Vegetarians can use cooked Quorn pieces or fillets.
- Try adding thinly sliced mushrooms, chopped tomatoes or even some diced pumpkin or butternut squash to vary the flavour and texture. Be adventurous with your cooking and the ingredients you choose – it's good to experiment.

Olive baked chicken

Preparation: 10 minutes
Cooking: 25 minutes
Serves: 2
Per serving: 255 kcal
41g protein
7g carbs
7g fat

60g (2oz) green olives, pitted
small bunch of fresh basil leaves
juice of ½ lemon
freshly ground black pepper
2 x 125g (4½oz) skinless, boneless chicken breasts
asparagus, baby carrots, new potatoes or salad, to serve

This is the perfect, no-fuss supper. You just prepare the aromatic topping, spread it over the chicken and leave it in the oven to bake – nothing could be simpler.

1 Preheat the oven to 200°C, gas mark 6.

2 Put the olives, basil leaves and lemon juice in a blender or small food processor and then blend to a smooth paste. Season to taste with freshly ground black pepper.

3 Place the chicken breasts in a non-stick ovenproof dish or one that you've lined with non-stick parchment or greaseproof paper. Spread the olive and basil paste thickly on top of each chicken breast.

4 Bake in the preheated oven for approximately 25 minutes, or until the chicken is thoroughly cooked.

5 Serve the baked chicken immediately with new potatoes and some steamed or grilled vegetables or a crisp salad.

Tips

- If you don't have a blender or food processor, you can either use a hand-held electric blender or just pound the topping ingredients together in the traditional way in a pestle and mortar, although the mixture may have a rougher texture.
- This chicken also tastes good served cold on a hot summer's day. Leave it to cool thoroughly and then cover and refrigerate until needed. Cut the chicken into thick diagonal slices and serve with some couscous, grilled tomatoes and colourful peppers. Delicious!

Or...

- For a more tangy Mediterranean tapenade topping, use juicy black olives instead of green ones and blend or mash them with two anchovy fillets, 1 tablespoon capers, a garlic clove, a small bunch of parsley and some lemon juice.
- If you're really in a hurry, you could just top the chicken breasts with reduced-calorie green or red pesto before baking them.

Caribbean chicken with fruity black bean sauce

Preparation: 10 minutes
Cooking: 40 minutes
Serves: 2
Per serving:
449 kcal
51g protein
50g carbs
5g fat

150ml (¼ pint) chicken stock **or** LighterLife Savoury Stock
2 x 125g (4½oz) skinless, boneless chicken breasts
1 red pepper, deseeded and thinly sliced
2 spring onions, sliced
1 garlic clove, finely chopped
1 red chilli, deseeded and finely chopped
2 teaspoons finely chopped fresh root ginger
1 x 200g (7oz) can cubed pineapple in natural juice, drained
1 tablespoon mango chutney
1 teaspoon brown sugar
1 teaspoon curry paste
1 x 200g (7oz) can black beans, drained and rinsed
freshly ground black pepper
60g (2oz) long-grain or basmati rice
2 tablespoons chopped fresh coriander

Bring the exotic flavours of the Caribbean into your home with this colourful West Indian recipe. It works equally well with turkey, and you could substitute some fresh juicy papaya or mango for the pineapple.

1 Preheat the oven to 180°C, gas mark 4.

2 Set a heavy-based frying pan over a medium heat, add a little of the stock and cook the chicken breasts for 5–7 minutes each side, until browned. Transfer the chicken to an ovenproof dish.

3 Add the red pepper, spring onions, garlic, chilli and ginger to the frying pan, and cook gently for about 5 minutes, until the onions are tender, adding more stock if necessary.

4 Stir in the remaining stock, together with the pineapple, mango chutney, brown sugar and curry paste. Bring to a simmer and then pour the mixture over the chicken.

5 Bake, uncovered, in the preheated oven for 15 minutes, until the chicken is cooked through. Lift out the chicken and keep warm.

6 Pour the pineapple and vegetable mixture back into the frying pan and bring to the boil. Simmer, stirring constantly, until the sauce has thickened. Add the drained black beans, and cook over a medium heat for 2–3 minutes. Season to taste with freshly ground black pepper.

7 Meanwhile, cook the rice according to the packet instructions. Drain well and fluff up with a fork.

8 To serve, spoon the pineapple-bean mixture over the chicken, sprinkle with chopped coriander and serve with the rice.

Tips

● Pickled jalapeno peppers work well in this recipe – just chop about six of them and add with the black beans. If you don't enjoy spicy foods, omit the chilli altogether; the chicken will still taste delicious.
● For a nutty flavour and more fibre, substitute brown rice for white.

Or...

For an even better flavour, use fresh instead of canned pineapple. Take a fresh small pineapple, remove the rind and inner hard core. Cut half of it into cubes and add to the sauce as outlined above. Eat the remaining pineapple as a refreshing dessert with low-fat yoghurt and berry fruits.

Chicken ratatouille

Preparation: 10 minutes
Cooking: 45 minutes
Serves: 2
Per serving:
272 kcal
44g protein
15g carbs
4g fat

250ml (8fl oz) chicken stock **or**
LighterLife Savoury Stock
1 onion, chopped
2 garlic cloves, crushed
2 x 125g (4½oz) boneless chicken
breasts, skinned and cut into strips
1 red pepper, deseeded and cut
into strips
1 courgette, sliced
1 aubergine, cut into 2.5cm
(1in) cubes
1 x 400g (14oz) can chopped
tomatoes
2 tablespoons tomato purée
pinch of sugar
2 tablespoons chopped basil
freshly ground black pepper

This is a variation on a classic dish from the south of France, evocative of sunny Mediterranean meals. In summer, when tomatoes are cheap, fragrant and more likely to be sun-ripened, you can use fresh ones instead of canned for a more authentic flavour.

1 Add a few spoonfuls of stock to a heavy-based frying pan and place over a low heat. When the pan is hot, add the onion and garlic and cook gently for about 10 minutes, until the onion is softened and golden.

2 Add the chicken strips, red pepper, courgette and aubergine and continue cooking, adding a little more stock if necessary, until they begin to brown.

3 Pour in the remaining stock, and stir in the tomatoes, tomato purée, sugar and basil. Cover the pan and simmer gently for 15 minutes. Stir well and then simmer, uncovered, for a further 15 minutes, until the sauce thickens and all the liquid is absorbed. Season with black pepper.

4 Serve the ratatouille hot with thin French beans or steamed green vegetables and plain boiled rice.

Tip

For the classic vegetarian version, just leave out the chicken and serve with rice as above, or use as a sauce for pasta, topped with grated Parmesan cheese. This also tastes good as an accompaniment to cottage cheese. You could also substitute Quorn pieces for the chicken.

Or...

You can eat the ratatouille cold, if preferred, with a crisp green or mixed salad. Let it cool thoroughly after cooking, and then transfer to a sealed container and refrigerate until you are ready to eat.

success story

George
lost 16 inches from his waist in six months

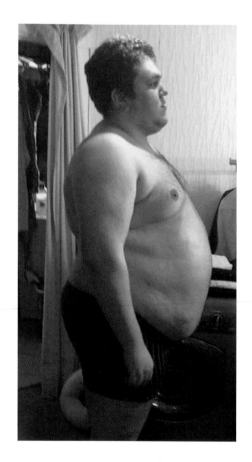

George
Waist size then: 54in
Waist size now: 38in

"I'd given up trying to lose weight until a friend recommended LighterLife. I was addicted to food and used to tell people I was cutting down while I was secretly bingeing. I'd also left my job as a trainee accountant. It didn't help that my ex-colleagues used to make fun of my size. They'd send me downstairs to get files, so they could see me come back sweating and out of breath.

My family is Greek and feasting is part of our culture. Mum's a great cook and she'd often make big portions of things like souvlaki with chips, and oven-baked pasta. She'd add flavour to things with lashings of halloumi cheese and oil. Even the average Greek salad is usually laden with salt and feta.

I used to blame Mum for making me fat, but through my LighterLife group work I learnt to take responsibility for my life and stop blaming other people for my weight problem. I also realised I was an 'emotional eater'. If I'd had a row with Mum or felt depressed I'd demolish a round of sandwiches. I'd be in such a hurry to get the sandwich into my mouth I wouldn't add butter, I'd just slap

some salami and cheese between two slices of bread and stuff them in without really tasting anything. The fact I grew up above a fish and chip shop didn't help much either. I was forever wolfing down the profits!

Since losing 16 inches from my waist with LighterLife I feel like a new man, both inside and out. I seize the day and have really got into fitness. I do lots of weight training at the gym whereas I used to feel far too self-conscious to try it before because I was so big. I completed the London Marathon in April 2010, which is quite a turnaround for someone who used to struggle to walk to the bus stop!

Like many people with a healthy weight, I watch my intake now and if I overdo it one day I'll cut back the next. It's all about balance. If all fails, I go clubbing and dance off the calories, which is great fun!"

www.lighterlife.com

George, now
a 38in waist

beef, lamb and pork

Low-fat cooking techniques and lean cuts make beef, lamb and pork dishes a healthy option.

With breeding and feed changes and the development of modern butchery techniques, beef, lamb and pork are lower in fat, particularly saturated fat, than ever before. The leanest types of red meat have less than ten per cent fat these days, compared to around 25 per cent back in the 1970s.

By swapping cuts and using different cooking methods, you can easily decrease your fat intake even further without sacrificing taste. Here are some suggestions:

- Grilled back bacon rashers with the fat trimmed off provide less than half the amount of fat than grilled streaky bacon, and less energy – 12.3g fat and 214 kcal, compared with 26.9g fat and 337 kcal per 100g.

58

- Extra-lean beef mince provides less fat and less energy than standard beef mince – 8.7g fat and 177 kcal, compared with 13.5g fat and 209 kcal per 100g.
- Roasted pork leg provides far less fat and energy than grilled pork belly – 5.5g fat and 182 kcal, compared with 23.4g fat and 320 kcal.

All this is great news because meat is a good source of protein, vitamins and minerals, including iron, selenium, zinc and B vitamins – particularly B12, which is vital for a healthy nervous system and red blood cell production and which you don't get from plant foods. Red meat is also now recognised as an important dietary source of vitamin D, which has lots of important functions, including building healthy bones and teeth.

Our tasty dishes include classics like Italian beef and macaroni bake and Irish stew, as well as more unusual ideas, such as spicy stuffed papaya – and many recipes can be adapted for vegetarians, too.

Boosting your iron intake

Red meat is rich in haem iron, which your body can absorb far more easily than the non-haem iron found in plant foods, such as beans, lentils, dark-green leafy vegetables, grains and fortified breakfast cereals. Tannin in tea and caffeine in coffee can further reduce your body's ability to absorb non-haem iron from grains and cereals. You can boost your take-up of non-haem iron from plant foods by eating them at the same time as food or drinks rich in vitamin C, such as strawberries, kiwis, oranges, peppers or a small glass of 100 per cent fruit juice. Eating them with red meat also has the same effect, so meat and two veg are a pretty sound idea!

Lamb with apricots and couscous

Preparation: 15 minutes
Cooking: 1¼ hours
Serves: 2
Per serving:
761 kcal
57g protein
77g carbs
25g fat

250g (9oz) lean stewing lamb
(all visible fat removed), cubed
1 teaspoon ground cinnamon
2 teaspoons ground cumin
2 teaspoons ground ginger
2 teaspoons ground turmeric
1 onion, chopped
1 garlic clove, crushed
350ml (12fl oz) stock **or** LighterLife
Savoury Stock
1 x 400g (14oz) can chopped
tomatoes
1 x 400g (14oz) can chickpeas,
drained and rinsed
30g (1oz) dried apricots, chopped
85g (3oz) couscous
seeds of 1 pomegranate (optional)
a handful of chopped coriander
freshly ground black pepper

Don't be put off by the list of spices in this recipe – it tastes delicious and looks really beautiful, especially if you add the ruby-red pomegranate seeds. In North Africa and the Middle East, lamb is frequently cooked with dried fruit and spices for their distinctive flavours.

1 Place a large non-stick pan over a medium heat and add the lamb. Cook for a few minutes, turning it until browned all over. Stir in the cinnamon, cumin, ginger and turmeric. Add the onion and garlic and 2 tablespoons of stock. Cook for 5 minutes, until the onion is softened.

2 When the onion starts to soften, add the tomatoes, chickpeas and apricots and 200ml (7fl oz) of stock. Bring to the boil, then reduce the heat and simmer for 1 hour, or until the meat is tender, stirring occasionally. Add a little water if the sauce reduces too much.

3 Meanwhile, bring the rest of the stock to the boil and pour over the couscous. Cover with cling film or a plate and leave for 10 minutes. Fluff it up with a fork and mix in the pomegranate seeds and coriander.

4 Check the seasoning, adding black pepper if necessary. Divide the couscous between two plates and ladle the lamb mixture over the top.

Tips

- Instead of simmering the lamb on the hob you could start it off in a flameproof casserole and then transfer it to a preheated oven after adding the tomatoes, stock and apricots. The dish can be happily left at 150°C, gas mark 2 for 2 hours while you get on with other things.
- Deseeding a pomegranate can be messy and the juice stains, so try this easy method. Cut down through the crown of the pomegranate with a sharp knife, pulling the two halves apart with your fingers. Then cut down through each half in the same way, so you have four quarters. Working over a bowl of water, use your fingers to separate the seeds from the membranes and skin. The seeds will sink to the bottom of the bowl, and the unwanted membrane and skin will float on the top. You can strain the seeds in a sieve, pat dry with kitchen paper and then stir them into the couscous.

Or...

This recipe works equally well with chicken, and will not take so long to cook. Add red, yellow or green peppers to make it even more colourful and serve with a dash of fiery harissa paste (available from most supermarkets, Middle Eastern stores and delicatessens).

Irish stew

Preparation: 15 minutes
Cooking: 2–2½ hours
Serves: 2
Per serving:
454 kcal
42g protein
22g carbs
22g fat

2 large potatoes, peeled and thinly sliced

300g (10oz) boned lean lamb (all visible fat removed), cut into chunks

1 large onion, thinly sliced

4 carrots, sliced

freshly ground black pepper

300ml (½ pint) stock **or** LighterLife Savoury Stock

chopped fresh parsley, spring onions or chives, to garnish

This traditional winter dish is really easy to prepare and cook, and a very welcoming way to warm you up on a cold day. Make sure you use a really lean cut of lamb, such as loin chops or leg steak.

1 In a heavy-based saucepan with a well-fitting lid, layer up all the ingredients, starting with a layer of potatoes and then adding a layer of lamb, followed by the onion and carrots. Continue layering in this way, grinding a little black pepper between the layers, until everything is used up, finishing with a topping of overlapping potatoes.

2 Pour in the stock, cover the pan and cook gently over a very low heat for about 2–2½ hours, until the meat is meltingly tender and the stew has thickened. If you want to brown the top, pop the pan under a hot grill.

3 Serve the stew immediately, sprinkled with chopped parsley, spring onions or chives, with steamed green vegetables, such as broccoli, cabbage, spring greens or French beans.

Tip

This dish can also be cooked for 6–8 hours in a slow cooker. All you need do is assemble it in the morning and you'll have a tasty meal ready and waiting for you in the evening.

Or...

Layer up the meat and vegetables in a casserole dish, and cook in a low preheated oven at 150°C, gas mark 2 for 2–3 hours. Remove the lid and then increase the oven temperature to 200°C, gas mark 6 for the last 20 minutes to brown the potato topping.

Lamb kebabs
with tabbouleh

Preparation: 15 minutes
Marinating/soaking: 15 minutes
Cooking: 15 minutes
Serves: 2
Per serving:
452 kcal
37g protein
31g carbs
20g fat

250g (9oz) lean lamb (all visible fat
removed), cubed
juice of ½ lemon
1 garlic clove, crushed
1 teaspoon chopped oregano **or**
marjoram
freshly ground black pepper
1 small red onion, cut into wedges
½ red pepper, deseeded and cut
into pieces
½ yellow pepper, deseeded and cut
into pieces
low-fat natural yoghurt or tzatziki,
to serve

Tabbouleh
60g (2oz) bulgar wheat
¼ red onion, chopped
2 ripe tomatoes, chopped
¼ small cucumber, diced
juice of 1 lemon
small bunch of mint or parsley,
chopped
freshly ground black pepper

This colourful dish is a typical example of healthy Mediterranean food. You can prepare the tabbouleh in advance and chill it in the fridge, and even the kebabs can be marinated and assembled the day before and refrigerated until you're ready to cook. On hot summer days, they taste even better grilled over hot coals on a barbecue in the garden.

1 Put the lamb in a bowl and add the lemon juice, garlic and oregano. Season with black pepper and stir well. Set aside to marinate for 15 minutes while you make the tabbouleh.

2 Put the bulgar wheat in a bowl and pour enough boiling water over the top to cover it. Cover the bowl and leave for 15 minutes, until the bulgar wheat has absorbed all the water and softened.

3 Drain off any excess water, and mix in the red onion, tomatoes, cucumber, lemon juice and herbs. Season with freshly ground black pepper. Chill in the refrigerator until required.

4 Thread the lamb alternately on to four kebab skewers with the red onion wedges and red and yellow pepper pieces. Brush with any leftover marinade and place on a foil-lined grill pan.

5 Cook under a hot grill for 15 minutes, turning occasionally, until the lamb is cooked to your liking and the vegetables are slightly charred and tender. Serve with the tabbouleh and a crisp green salad with some low-fat natural yoghurt or tzatziki (see page 104) on the side.

Tip

If you don't have red onions, use an ordinary white one for the kebabs, and spring onions for the tabbouleh.

Or...

- You can use couscous instead of bulgar wheat. Soak in boiling water in the same way.
- Vegetarians can omit the lamb and load more vegetables onto the skewers – try button mushrooms, chunks of courgette or aubergine, small corn cobs and cherry tomatoes or even some halloumi cheese.

Stir-fried pork and noodles

Preparation: 10 minutes
Marinating: 10 minutes
Cooking: 10–12 minutes
Serves: 2
Per serving:
276 kcal
32g protein
19g carbs
8g fat

1 tablespoon soy sauce
1 teaspoon Worcestershire sauce
1 tablespoon oyster sauce
1 onion, chopped
1 garlic clove, crushed
175g (6oz) lean pork steaks
(all visible fat removed), cut into
thin strips
100g (3½oz) dried medium
egg noodles
1 carrot, cut into matchstick strips
60g (2oz) mangetout, halved
½ red pepper, deseeded and cut into
thin strips
3 tablespoons stock or LighterLife
Savoury Stock
freshly ground black pepper
torn coriander leaves or snipped
chives, to garnish

This colourful Chinese stir-fry can be prepared and cooked in minutes, making it a perfect supper dish. It's important to use really good-quality lean pork – steaks or tenderloin (fillet) are best.

1 Mix together the soy sauce, Worcestershire sauce, oyster sauce, chopped onion and garlic in a flat dish. Add the pork strips to this marinade and stir to coat well. Cover and refrigerate for 10 minutes.

2 Meanwhile, cook the egg noodles according to the instructions on the packet, and then drain in a colander and set aside.

3 Place a non-stick wok or deep frying pan over a medium heat. When the pan is hot, add the pork and its marinade and stir-fry briskly for 4 minutes. Stir in the carrot, mangetout and red pepper, and stir-fry for 2–3 minutes. The vegetables should be a little tender but still crunchy.

4 Finally, add the stock, then stir in the cooked egg noodles and heat through gently. Season to taste with black pepper.

5 Serve immediately in warmed bowls, sprinkled with torn coriander leaves or snipped chives.

Tip

To stop cooked noodles sticking together while they're draining, rinse them briefly in cold water. This makes them easier to stir-fry afterwards.

Or...

If you like hot spicy food, try adding a chopped fresh red chilli or some hot chilli flakes to the marinade. Vary the flavours by adding halved thin green beans, sugar snap peas, strips of yellow pepper or sliced spring onions. You could even substitute rice noodles for the egg ones we used.

Pork chops with baked parsnip strips

Preparation: 5 minutes
Soaking: 10–15 minutes
Cooking: 30 minutes
Serves: 2
Per serving:
261 kcal
38g protein
7g carbs
9g fat

2 parsnips
250ml (8fl oz) vegetable stock or LighterLife Savoury Stock
2 x 115g (4oz) pork loin chops, all visible fat removed
sprig of rosemary
freshly ground black pepper

The flavours of pork and parsnips marry well together and make a nutritious easy meal. If you don't have any parsnips or want a great variation, you could use some sweet potatoes instead. Naturally sweet and a beautiful orange colour, they'll taste just as good.

1 Preheat the oven to 200°C, gas mark 6.

2 Peel the parsnips and cut off the woody ends. Using the potato peeler, slice them lengthways into long flat strips. Soak the parsnip strips in a bowl of hot stock for 10–15 minutes. Remove and drain.

3 Put the pork chops on a baking tray. Strip the leaves from the sprig of rosemary and sprinkle them over the pork. Season with freshly ground black pepper and then bake in the preheated oven for about 10–12 minutes. Turn the pork chops over and bake for a further 10–12 minutes until golden brown. Check that they don't overcook.

4 Meanwhile, line another baking tray with non-stick paper and arrange the drained parsnip strips on it. Bake for 10–15 minutes, turning them occasionally, until the parsnips are golden brown. You'll need to keep an eye on them, as they can burn easily.

5 Serve the pork and caramelized parsnips immediately with a mixed salad or some steamed green vegetables.

Tip

To make a tasty sauce, simmer the stock in which the parsnips were soaked for 15 minutes, until reduced. Delicious! To make it creamy, let it cool a little and stir in a spoonful of plain virtually fat-free fromage frais.

Or...

If preferred, you can slice the parsnips as thinly as possible with a knife and then, instead of soaking them, parboil them in a small pan of boiling stock for about 5 minutes, until they start to soften. Remove, drain and bake as outlined above. This may be a better cooking method for older, woody parsnips, which are no longer tender.

Apricot-stuffed pork on celeriac patties

Preparation: 15 minutes
Cooking: 25–30 minutes
Serves: 2
Per serving:
422 kcal
50g protein
24g carbs
14g fat

250g (9oz) lean pork fillet, all visible fat removed
60g/2oz half-fat soft cheese
4 ready-to-eat dried apricots, chopped
1 tablespoon chopped sage
freshly ground black pepper
2 wafer-thin slices Parma ham, all visible fat removed

Celeriac patties
1 medium celeriac
squeeze of lemon juice
1 large potato
1 small onion
1 tablespoon finely chopped parsley
freshly ground black pepper
1–2 tablespoons beaten egg

Pork fillet (or tenderloin as it's sometimes known) is extremely lean and very satisfying. Stuffing it with a tasty filling is not only easy to do but also a great way to make it more interesting and nutritious. This is an eye-catching dish when you want to impress!

1 Preheat the oven to 190°C, gas mark 5.

2 Make the celeriac patties: cut off the hard outer covering from the celeriac. Grate the celeriac into a bowl, adding a squeeze of lemon juice to prevent it discolouring. Peel and grate the potato, and grate the onion, and then add them both to the celeriac.

3 Stir in the parsley and mix well. Grind in some black pepper and add a little beaten egg; go easy as you only need enough to bind the mixture together – it shouldn't be too wet or the patties will fall apart. Divide into four portions and place on a baking tray, lined with non-stick baking paper. Press down lightly with a slice to form four flat patties.

4 Take the pork fillet and make a deep incision along it lengthways without cutting all the way through. Open it up and flatten it. Mix the soft cheese with the apricots, sage and black pepper, and spread it over the pork. Fold the pork over the top of the filling to enclose it and wrap the Parma ham around it. Place on a non-stick baking tray.

5 Put the pork and the patties in the preheated oven and cook for 25–30 minutes, turning the patties once. The patties should be crisp and golden brown, and the pork should be cooked through and no longer pink.

6 Cut the pork into slices and arrange on two serving plates with the celeriac patties. Serve with salad and some grilled tomatoes.

Tip

Celeriac can discolour if not used quickly. If you want to grate it in advance, put it into a bowl of cold water immediately with a squeeze of lemon juice or a drop of white wine vinegar.

Or...

● Try adding different herbs to the patties – a mixture of chopped mint and coriander tastes good, especially if served with lamb steaks.
● Make a filling for the pork with prunes, fresh apricots or sun-dried tomatoes (not in oil) mixed into the soft cheese with herbs.

Beef and noodle soup

Preparation: 15 minutes
Cooking: 15 minutes
Serves: 2
Per serving:
366 kcal
51g protein
18g carbs
10g fat

300ml (½ pint) beef stock **or**
LighterLife Savoury Stock

1cm (½in) piece fresh root ginger,
peeled and finely sliced

1 garlic clove, sliced

½ red chilli, thinly sliced

1 lemongrass stalk, halved

4 sprigs of purple sprouting broccoli,
halved lengthways and woody
stalks removed

6 baby corn, halved lengthways

½ red pepper, deseeded
and thinly sliced

100g (3½oz) medium dried
egg noodles

300g (10oz) lean rump steak
(all visible fat removed), cut into
thin strips

1 tablespoon miso paste

lime wedges, to serve

This is a substantial meal in a bowl rather than just a soup. It's packed with nutritional goodness and will warm you up on a cold day. You might even want to consider freezing a portion to reheat at a later date when you don't have much time to cook.

1 Put the stock in a saucepan with the ginger, garlic, chilli and lemongrass. Cover the pan, then place over a low heat and bring slowly to a gentle simmer.

2 Add the broccoli, baby corn and red pepper and cook for 5 minutes, or until the vegetables are just tender.

3 Meanwhile, cook the egg noodles, according to the instructions on the packet, and then drain them in a colander.

4 Add the strips of rump steak and miso paste to the soup in the pan and cook gently for 2–3 minutes.

5 To serve, divide the noodles between two large shallow soup bowls. Discard the lemongrass and ladle the hot soup into the bowls. Serve immediately with a lime wedge.

Tips

● Purple sprouting broccoli is at its best between March and May. If you buy it out of season you can end up with really tough woody stalks. For the rest of the year, substitute small broccoli florets or even shredded spring greens or pak choi.

● Miso paste is available from most supermarkets as well as delicatessens, but don't worry if you can't get hold of it – this soup will still taste great without it.

Or...

● Have fun experimenting with different flavours, depending on what's in the fridge or store cupboard. Try chicken instead of steak and add sliced mushrooms and a dash of soy sauce instead of miso paste.

● If you're vegetarian, you can use tofu cubes instead of beef.

72

Spicy stuffed papaya

Preparation: 15 minutes
Cooking: 40 minutes
Serves: 2
Per serving:
304 kcal
32g protein
17g carbs
12g fat

2 tablespoons stock **or LighterLife Savoury Stock**

4 spring onions, sliced

1 garlic clove, crushed

225g (8oz) lean minced beef (max. 5% fat)

1 large ripe papaya

2 tomatoes, skinned and chopped

½ fresh red chilli, finely chopped

1 tablespoon sultanas

pinch of ground allspice

1 tablespoon chopped parsley

1 tablespoon finely grated Parmesan cheese

1 tablespoon fresh breadcrumbs

freshly ground black pepper

This sounds unusual but don't be put off by the papaya in this recipe – it's a really delicious and healthy way of cooking spicy mince. Papayas contain antioxidants and are a very good source of vitamins C and E.

1 Preheat the oven to 180°C, gas mark 4.

2 Heat the stock in a frying pan, add the spring onions and cook for 2–3 minutes, until they're softened. Add the garlic and minced beef and cook over a medium heat until the mince is browned all over.

3 Meanwhile, cut the papaya in half lengthways and remove the seeds. Scoop out some of the papaya flesh, leaving about 1cm (½in) around the edge. Dice the scooped-out flesh.

4 Add the diced papaya, tomato, chilli, sultanas, allspice and parsley to the minced beef, and cook gently until any liquid has been absorbed.

5 Put the papaya shells in a shallow ovenproof dish, and fill with the beef mixture. Pour some boiling water into the dish around the stuffed papayas, so it comes one-quarter of the way up them. Mix the grated Parmesan, breadcrumbs and black pepper together and sprinkle over the stuffed papayas.

6 Bake in the preheated oven for 20–25 minutes, until the topping is crisp and golden brown. Serve the stuffed papayas immediately with some boiled rice or noodles and a crisp salad.

Tip

You can make fresh breadcrumbs by blitzing some one-day-old white or wholemeal bread in a blender or food processor (see page 32).

Or...

You can use this filling as a stuffing for peppers, aubergines and other vegetables. If you're vegetarian, omit the minced beef and make a filling with Quorn mince, cooked rice or couscous mixed with chopped papaya, spring onions, tomatoes and sultanas. Flavour it with chilli and spices or herbs and use the same topping ingredients before baking.

Steak and vegetable towers

Preparation: 10 minutes
Cooking: 15 minutes
Serves: 2
Per serving:
313 kcal
51g protein
7g carbs
9g fat

3 tablespoons beef stock **or** LighterLife Savoury Stock

1 red onion, thinly sliced

2 large portobello mushrooms, stalks removed

2 courgettes, thickly sliced

2 x 150g (5oz) lean fillet steaks, all visible fat removed

1 ripe beefsteak tomato, cut into thick slices

freshly ground black pepper

watercress or rocket leaves, to garnish

few drops of balsamic vinegar

This dish may look elaborate but it's actually very quick and easy to make, and great for special occasions. If you feel adventurous, experiment with different colourful vegetables, such as sliced aubergine and grilled peppers.

1 Heat the stock in a frying pan and add the sliced red onion. Cook very gently over a low heat until the stock evaporates and the onion is really tender and slightly caramelized. Remove from the pan, then set aside and keep warm.

2 Place the mushrooms and courgette slices in the pan juices and cook for a few minutes on each side, until tender. Alternatively, cook them on a hot ridged grill pan.

3 Meanwhile, grill the fillet steaks on a hot, ridged, cast-iron grill pan or under a preheated hot grill until cooked on both sides.

4 To assemble each tower, place a slice of tomato on each serving plate, put a cooked mushroom on top and fill with the cooked red onion. Add a grinding of black pepper and put a slice of tomato and another of courgette on top. Cover with the cooked steak and the remaining courgette and tomato slices. Arrange a little pile of rocket or watercress on top and sprinkle with balsamic vinegar, or scatter it around the tower on the plate.

5 Serve with some steamed or boiled green beans or broccoli and a small baked potato, topped, if wished, with a spoonful of virtually fat-free fromage frais.

Tip

To make sure your steaks are perfectly cooked to your liking every time, follow this simple guide:
- Grill for 2–3 minutes each side for rare
- Grill for 4–5 minutes each side for medium
- Grill for 5–6 minutes each side for well done.

Or...

- You could grill the tomato slices instead of adding them raw.
- Make a delicious vegetarian version by adding more mushrooms and substituting slices of grilled halloumi cheese for the steak.

Italian beef and macaroni bake

Preparation: 10 minutes
Cooking: 55 minutes
Serves: 2
Per serving:
323 kcal
33g protein
23g carbs
11g fat

100g (3½oz) macaroni
1 onion, finely chopped
1 garlic clove, crushed
60ml (2fl oz) beef stock **or** LighterLife Savoury Stock
175g (6oz) lean minced beef (max. 5% fat)
250ml (9fl oz) passata
pinch of sugar
small bunch of fresh basil, chopped

White sauce
1 tablespoon cornflour
250ml (9fl oz) skimmed milk
2 tablespoons virtually fat-free fromage frais
pinch of ground nutmeg
1 egg, beaten
freshly ground black pepper

Although this takes a little while to cook, it's easy to prepare and utilizes basic store cupboard ingredients. We've used macaroni but it works with any dried pasta shapes. It freezes well, so you can prepare it in advance, add the white sauce, then cool and freeze. To serve, defrost and cook in a preheated oven as below.

1 Preheat the oven to 180°C, gas mark 4.

2 Cook the pasta in a large saucepan of boiling water, according to the instructions on the packet, until it's tender but still retains a little bite *(al dente)*. Drain well in a colander.

3 Meanwhile, cook the onion and garlic in the stock until softened. Stir in the minced beef and cook for 5–10 minutes, stirring occasionally. Add the passata, sugar and basil and mix well. Simmer for 15 minutes.

4 While the mince is cooking, make the white sauce. Blend the cornflour and a little of the milk together. Heat the remaining milk in a non-stick pan and bring to the boil. Stir the hot milk into the cornflour mixture and return to the pan. Heat gently, stirring all the time, until it thickens. Remove from the heat and then stir in the fromage frais, ground nutmeg and beaten egg. Season with black pepper.

5 Cover the base of an ovenproof dish with half of the cooked pasta. Spoon the meat mixture over the pasta and then cover with the remaining pasta. Pour the white sauce over the top.

6 Bake in the preheated oven for about 30 minutes, until bubbling and golden brown. Serve immediately with a crisp salad.

Tip

If you don't have any passata, just use some canned chopped tomatoes instead. The tomato sauce will not be as smooth but it will make no difference to the flavour of the finished dish.

Or...

- For additional flavour and a crisp topping, sprinkle a tablespoon of grated Parmesan over the top before cooking.
- Make a delicious vegetarian version of this dish. Omit the mince and add roasted peppers, courgettes and aubergines to the tomato sauce. Layer with the pasta, cover with white sauce and bake as above.

Chilli con carne

Preparation: 10 minutes
Cooking: 30 minutes
Serves: 2
Per serving:
531 kcal
53g protein
46g carbs
15g fat

250g (9oz) lean beef mince
(max 5% fat)
1 onion, finely chopped
2 garlic cloves, crushed
1 x 400g (14fl oz) can chopped
tomatoes
1 teaspoon paprika
1 teaspoon chilli powder
1 teaspoon cayenne pepper
1 x 400g (14oz) can kidney beans,
drained and rinsed
freshly ground black pepper
30g (1oz) coarsely grated half-fat
Cheddar cheese (optional)
handful of fresh coriander, chopped
shredded chilli, to garnish (optional)
2 heaped tablespoons guacamole
(see page 138)
2 tablespoons virtually fat-free
fromage frais

If you enjoy Tex-Mex food, chilli con carne is simple to make and you can garnish it in a variety of ways. We've gone easy on the chilli powder but if you're a chilli afficionado and love hot, spicy food, just increase the quantity or, better still, cook a chopped jalapeno chilli with the mince, onion and garlic. You can even garnish the finished dish with shredded chillies!

1 Put the minced beef, onion and garlic in a large saucepan and cook over a medium heat for about 5 minutes, until the onion is softened and the mince is browned and crumbly.

2 Add the chopped tomatoes, paprika, chilli powder and cayenne pepper. Stir well and simmer gently for 20 minutes.

3 Stir in the drained kidney beans and simmer for a further 5 minutes, until the sauce is rich and thickened. Season to taste with black pepper and add more chilli powder if you like it hot.

4 Divide the chilli con carne between two serving plates. Sprinkle with the grated cheese (if using), coriander and chilli (optional), and add a spoonful of guacamole and fromage frais to each serving. Serve with plain boiled rice and a crisp salad.

Tip

To get the most flavour from your garlic, finely grate it or crush it in a garlic press instead of chopping it. This releases more of the juices, adding more flavour to the dish.

Or...

Cook the chilli a little longer until the sauce really reduces and thickens, and place a couple of spoonfuls on some shredded crisp iceberg lettuce leaves on a warmed tortilla. Top with salsa or guacamole (see recipes on page 138) and fromage frais, then roll up and eat in your fingers. Or you can use the chilli con carne as a hot filling for tacos. Absolutely fabulous!

success story

Claire

lost six dress sizes in six months

Claire
Dress size before: 22
Dress size now: 10

" I was an obese child and hated being the 'big girl' in my class. My mum took me to the school GP when I was nine to try to tackle the problem. He advised her to prepare packed lunches for me to take to school, so I didn't eat the stodgy school food. But it didn't work.

As an adult, I tried to lose weight but would ruin any good work with secret eating. I would have been mortified if people knew just how much I was putting away; it was like an addiction. When I was eating I could zone out, and just be suspended in a delicious, comforting place. Then afterwards I'd feel terrible.

I'd do things like stop at the garage and get snacks, such as sausage rolls, chocolate or pasties, disposing of the wrappers before I got home, so my partner didn't find out. I'd snack all evening and make sure any wrappers or leftovers went way down into the dustbin so no one would find the evidence. It was a horrible way to live. Generally speaking, it wasn't that I ate the wrong things, I just ate too much of everything.

I started LighterLife because my hairdresser, Sarah, was on Total and she was losing weight really fast. I wanted what she had. In a way, being on Total gave me the chance to start my dietary life all over again. In my group, I was able to talk about the secret eating, and it was a relief to hear similar stories from other people and realise how common such behaviour could be.

When I started reintroducing conventional food after reaching my goal weight, I felt like a baby discovering food and taste for the first time. It was exciting but also a little daunting. I was a bit worried I'd lose control but the Programme was so structured, and my group were so supportive, that I enjoyed the transition to conventional food.

My palate is much sharper now. For instance, I can't eat chips from a chip shop any more because they taste like they've been fried in cheap oil. Funnily enough, I love mushrooms, which I used to loathe. I've also discovered the joys of spicy Moroccan food; I used to steer clear of anything like that. I also practise what I call 'mindfulness' with my eating. I'm aware of everything I put into my mouth and take time to taste and chew it.

Today, I use food as fuel, not to relieve boredom or stress. I'm so grateful for my LighterLife journey that I've trained as an Associate Counsellor for the Newbury area and would highly recommend LighterLife to anyone who needs to lose weight. 99

www.lighterlife.com

Claire, now a size 10

vegetarian

> "I am better off with vegetables at the bottom of my garden than with all the fairies of the Midsummer Night's Dream."
>
> Dorothy L. Sayers, crime novelist

In this chapter, there are fresh, tasty soups and salads and satisfying veggie main courses for everyone to enjoy.

Brighten up your veggie choices with our tasty recipes, including spicy pasta arrabbiata, risotto primavera and delicious veggie burgers, which vegetarians and meat lovers alike will love.

Health experts recommend eating at least five servings of vegetables and fruit a day – that's at least five lots in total, not five fruit plus five veg – to help reduce the risk of health problems, including strokes, heart disease and type 2 diabetes. A serving is 80g (3oz) of vegetables or fruit, which is far smaller than you would imagine – roughly a decent handful.

84

Eating fruit and vegetables can help you stay healthy and at a healthy weight because they're usually low in fat and energy, yet provide lots of fibre and a wide range of vitamins and minerals. Fresh, frozen, tinned, canned and dried vegetables (and fruit), along with juices, beans and pulses, all count towards your 5-a-day. Make the most of your veggie choices by buying seasonally and locally where you can. It's usually fresher than imported produce, generally tastes better, and is often far cheaper, too.

All our vegetarian dishes are easy to prepare, full of flavour and a great way of helping you get your 5-a-day – so give them pride of place on your table.

Note: There's lots of advice on 5-a-day at www.5aday.nhs.uk

Pulses

Canned and dried pulses (peas, beans and lentils) are rich in fibre, protein, iron and B vitamins. They're ideal for soups and casseroles, but remember that most dried pulses need to be soaked and cooked before use. Dried lentils are the handy exception: you can add them straight from the packet to thicken up a soup or casserole without any preparation. Canned beans can usually be eaten straight from the tin as they're already cooked.

Creamy spinach soup

Preparation: 10 minutes
Cooking: 45 minutes
Serves: 2
Per serving:
220 kcal
19g protein
25g carbs
5g fat

600ml (1 pint) vegetable stock **or**
LighterLife Savoury Stock
1 tablespoon soy sauce
1 onion, coarsely chopped
2 potatoes, peeled and diced
2 courgettes, thickly sliced
1kg (2lb) fresh spinach
freshly ground black pepper
2 tablespoons quark **or**
fromage frais
snipped chives, to garnish

Spinach is super-healthy and nutritious. It's packed with iron and is an excellent source of vitamins A, C, K and folate. A great source of lutein, it also helps to promote healthy vision. As well as adding it to soups and vegetable dishes or eating it cooked as a side vegetable, you can mix the tender baby leaves with rocket and watercress for use in salads.

1 Put 2 tablespoons of the stock with the soy sauce in a large heavy-based saucepan and set over a low to medium heat. Add the onion and cook for about 10 minutes, until softened and golden brown, taking care that it doesn't burn.

2 Add the remaining stock, along with the potatoes and courgettes. Bring to the boil, then reduce the heat, cover the pan and simmer gently for 30 minutes, or until the vegetables are tender.

3 Check the spinach to remove any tough stems. Add the spinach leaves to the pan and cook for a further 2 minutes. Remove the pan from the heat and season to taste with black pepper.

4 Purée the soup in batches in a blender or food processor. Return the soup to the saucepan and then heat through gently for 5 minutes.

5 Ladle the hot soup into two serving bowls, swirl in some quark or fromage frais and sprinkle with chives. Serve immediately.

Tips

- To really bring out the flavour of the spinach, add a squeeze of lemon juice to the hot soup before blending.
- If you're in a hurry, you can buy bags of prepared and washed baby spinach leaves. They will be more expensive but you won't have to spend time sorting through them and removing the stems.

Or...

Substitute watercress for the spinach – a couple of bunches will be plenty – and enjoy the distinctive, peppery flavour.

Provençal vegetable soup with pesto

Preparation: 15 minutes
Cooking: 35 minutes
Serves: 2
Per serving:
130 kcal
6g protein
22g carbs
2g fat

3 young carrots, thinly sliced or diced
85g (3oz) baby new potatoes, peeled and diced
1 stick celery, diced
1 garlic clove, crushed
600ml (1 pint) hot vegetable stock **or** LighterLife Savoury Stock
4 spring onions, trimmed and sliced
175g (6oz) ripe tomatoes, chopped
2 courgettes, diced
60g (2oz) fine green beans, trimmed and quartered
4 tablespoons chopped basil, tarragon or chives
freshly ground black pepper
2 teaspoons reduced-calorie green pesto

Packed full of natural goodness, this classic light soup from Provence is a great way of getting your 5-a-day. And it's simplicity itself to make, using a variety of fresh, seasonal vegetables and herbs for added taste.

1 Put the carrots, new potatoes, celery and garlic in a large saucepan. Add the hot vegetable stock and bring to the boil. Reduce the heat to a simmer and cook gently for 15 minutes.

2 Stir in the spring onions, tomatoes, courgettes, green beans and herbs. Leave to simmer for another 15 minutes, or until all the vegetables are cooked and tender.

3 Season to taste with freshly ground black pepper and ladle the hot soup into two serving bowls. Swirl in the pesto and serve.

Tip

If you use older carrots and potatoes, they may take a little longer to soften and cook than tender baby ones.

Or...

- You can vary the vegetables in this great soup, depending on what's in season. Try adding chopped asparagus spears, diced peppers or a small bunch of shredded watercress or baby spinach leaves.
- A colourful alternative is to stir some red pesto – instead of green – into the hot soup just before serving.

Sweet potato and watercress soup

Preparation: 10 minutes
Cooking: 25 minutes
Serves: 2
Per serving:
199 kcal
8g protein
35g carbs
3g fat

1 medium sweet potato,
peeled and diced

300ml (½ pint) vegetable stock **or**
LighterLife Savoury Stock

30g (1oz) red lentils

pinch of cayenne pepper

grated zest of ½ lemon

freshly ground black pepper

1 small bunch watercress,
roughly chopped

3 tablespoons snipped fresh chives

4 shavings Parmesan cheese,
to garnish

2 wholemeal pitta breads,
cut into strips

Nothing warms you up on a cold day like a bowl of hot vegetable soup. The lentils make this recipe very nourishing and filling. Try making double the quantity and freezing two portions for another meal.

1 Put the sweet potato in a saucepan with the hot stock and lentils. Add the cayenne pepper, then cover the pan and bring to the boil. Reduce the heat and simmer gently for 15 minutes, until the sweet potatoes are soft and the lentils have broken down.

2 Stir in the lemon zest and season to taste with black pepper. Remove the pan from the heat and then, in batches, blitz the soup in a blender or food processor, until smooth.

3 Return the soup to the saucepan and stir in the chopped watercress. Heat through gently for 5 minutes.

4 Ladle the hot soup into two large bowls. Scatter the snipped chives and Parmesan shavings over the top and serve with strips of pitta bread.

Tips

- The watercress gives the soup an attractive flecked appearance, but you can just add the whole sprigs before blending, if preferred.
- To save washing up, use a hand-held electric blender in the saucepan instead of transferring the soup to a blender or food processor.

Or...

If you don't have a sweet potato, just peel and dice a large baking potato and carrot instead. They will help to thicken the soup, giving it a smooth texture when blended – and a sweet flavour.

Spiced parsnip soup

Preparation: 10 minutes
Cooking: 30 minutes
Serves: 2
Per serving:
142g kcal
4g protein
27g carbs
2g fat

1 onion, finely chopped

1 red chilli, deseeded and finely chopped

250g (9oz) parsnips, trimmed, peeled and diced

1 tablespoon runny honey

600ml (1 pint) vegetable stock **or** LighterLife Savoury Stock

1 teaspoon garam masala

freshly ground black pepper

2 tablespoons fat-free natural yoghurt

2 teaspoons chopped parsley **or** some snipped chives

chopped red pepper, to garnish

Parsnips make a lovely, velvety, smooth-textured soup. You can buy them all the year round but they taste best in the winter after a heavy frost. The spices add warmth and heat to this light meal in a dish.

1 Put the onion, chilli, parsnips, honey and stock in a large saucepan. Bring to the boil, then cover the pan and simmer very gently for 15–20 minutes, until the vegetables are tender.

2 Pour the hot soup into a blender or food processor (you may have to do this in batches) and blend until thickened and smooth.

3 Return the soup to the pan, then stir in the garam masala and season to taste with some freshly ground black pepper. Warm through gently over a low heat for 5 minutes.

4 Ladle the hot soup into serving bowls and swirl in the yoghurt. Sprinkle with chives or parsley and chopped red pepper and serve immediately while it's still really hot.

Tip

If you don't have a sweet tooth, simply reduce the amount of honey to ½ tablespoon and add plenty of freshly ground black pepper.

Or...

- Try using a mixture of parsnips and carrots for a beautiful, richly coloured soup. Instead of garam masala, flavour it with ground nutmeg, cumin and turmeric, which will intensify the colour and enhance the spicy flavour.
- Alternatively, make a curried parsnip and apple soup. Just add an apple, which has been peeled, cored and diced, with the parsnip, and then flavour with curry powder for a spicy, sweet soup.
- Have fun experimenting with different toppings and garnishes. Why not try the following?
    Add a teaspoon of spicy salsa.
    Sprinkle with your favourite chopped herbs.
    Swirl in a teaspoon of reduced-calorie pesto.
    Sprinkle with a little grated cheese, such as Parmesan, Gruyère or half-fat Cheddar.

Mango, mint and sweet potato salad

Preparation: 15 minutes
Cooking: 12 minutes
Chilling: 1 hour
Serves: 2
Per serving:
105 kcal
2g protein
22g carbs
1g fat

1 small sweet potato
1 red pepper, deseeded and sliced
1 small ripe mango
2 spring onions, sliced
1 small lettuce
chopped fresh mint, to garnish

Minty dressing
2 tablespoons chopped fresh mint
juice of ½ lemon
1 teaspoon grated lemon zest
½ tablespoon balsamic vinegar

What makes this salad so enticing is its beautifully intense colour. It's cooling and refreshing on a hot summer's day and makes a great accompaniment to chicken or fish cooked over hot coals on a barbecue.

1 Peel the sweet potato and cut into slices. Place on a hot ridged grill pan with the red pepper and grill for 6 minutes, until softened and striped attractively. Turn over and cook the other side. Alternatively, you can cook the unpeeled sweet potato for 3–5 minutes in the microwave, until soft, or for 30–40 minutes in a preheated oven at 230°C, Gas Mark 8. Allow to cool before removing the skin and cutting into slices or chunks.

2 Stand the mango upright on a chopping board and slice down either side of the central stone with a sharp knife. Take each half and cut the flesh into thick slices, peeling away the skin from each slice. Cut the mango into cubes. Don't waste any of the juicy, succulent fruit – you can also cut away the soft flesh from the stone into small slices.

3 In a sealable container, mix the mango gently with the sweet potato and red pepper, taking care not to break the sweet potato up too much. Add the spring onions.

4 Blend the dressing ingredients and pour over the mango and sweet potato. Seal the container and leave in the fridge for 1 hour.

5 To serve, arrange the lettuce on two serving plates and top with the mango and sweet potato mixture. Sprinkle with chopped mint.

Tips

- Store mangoes at room temperature rather than in the fridge to make the most of their fragrant flavour. To check that a mango is ripe, squeeze it very gently – if it gives slightly, it is ready to eat.
- If you can only find waxed lemons, scrub the skin prior to grating to remove as much of the wax as possible. Don't grate right down to the white pith as it's mouth-puckeringly bitter.
- To skin a hot cooked sweet potato, puncture it with a sharp knife and you'll find the skin comes away very easily.

Or...

- Make an alternative dressing by mixing some low-fat natural yoghurt with a squeeze of lemon juice and a tablespoon of mango chutney.
- If you like spicy food, dust the sweet potato slices with a pinch each of ground cinnamon, nutmeg and cumin before grilling.

Mexican spicy bean tortiila wrap

Preparation: 10 minutes
Cooking: 2–5 minutes
Serves: 2
Per serving:
376 kcal
14g protein
53g carbs
12g fat

1 x 200g (7oz) can kidney beans, drained and rinsed

4 spring onions, sliced

¼ cucumber, diced

2 dessertspoons Mexican salsa (see recipe on page 138)

2 tablespoons chopped fresh coriander

freshly ground black pepper

2 wheat or corn tortillas

2 tablespoons low-fat natural yoghurt

few crisp lettuce leaves, shredded

2 tablespoons guacamole (see recipe on page 138)

Eat these sensational tortillas as a light meal or wrap them tightly in cling film and take them to work for a healthy packed lunch. Store in a cool box or the fridge until you're ready to eat them.

1 In a bowl, mix together the kidney beans, spring onions, cucumber and salsa. Stir in the chopped coriander and season to taste with black pepper.

2 Heat the tortillas for a few minutes on a hot griddle pan or in a preheated moderate oven, or for 15 seconds in a microwave – they should be warmed through, not charred or too dry.

3 Spread the yoghurt over the warm tortillas and cover with shredded lettuce. Divide the bean and salsa mixture between them.

4 Roll up the tortillas and serve with guacamole and some crisp salad or grilled vegetables.

Tip

To make these tortillas even more spicy, you can add some finely chopped chilli to the bean and salsa mixture.

Or...

- Use canned mixed beans or black beans instead of kidney beans and add 60g (2oz) reduced-fat feta cheese, cut into small cubes. Mix with the spring onions and cucumber and then substitute some sweet chilli sauce for the salsa.
- If you're a meat eater, stir some cubed cooked chicken breast into the beans and salsa filling.

Classic Italian vegetable frittata

Preparation: 10 minutes
Cooking: 25–30 minutes
Serves: 2
Per serving:
254 kcal
18g protein
14g carbs
14g fat

3 tablespoons vegetable stock **or**
LighterLife Savoury Stock
1 onion, thinly sliced
3 courgettes, thinly sliced
2 garlic cloves, crushed
4 tomatoes, chopped
4 medium eggs
freshly ground black pepper
2 tablespoons chopped parsley
2 teaspoons grated Parmesan
cheese
salad, to serve

A frittata is a versatile Italian omelette, which is cooked very slowly, then finished off under the grill and eaten in wedges. You can enjoy it hot from the pan, serve it lukewarm or even eat it cold. It's great choice for packed lunches and summer picnics.

1 Place a non-stick frying pan over a low heat. Add the stock and then the onion, courgettes and garlic, and cook gently, stirring from time to time, for about 5 minutes, until softened. Add the tomatoes and cook for 5 more minutes.

2 In a bowl, beat the eggs with a wire whisk until thoroughly combined, and season with freshly ground black pepper.

3 Pour the beaten eggs and chopped parsley into the vegetable mixture and stir gently. Cook over a very low heat for 15 minutes, or until the frittata is set underneath but still slightly runny on top. Sprinkle with grated Parmesan cheese.

4 Place the pan under a preheated hot grill for 2–3 minutes, until the top of the fritatta is set and golden brown.

5 Carefully slide the frittata out of the pan onto a plate and cut into wedges. Serve with a crisp salad or grilled vegetables of your choice.

Tip

To 'prove' an omelette pan and stop it sticking, just spray it lightly with a little olive oil and then sprinkle salt all over the base and a little way up the sides. Place over a moderate heat until it's smoking hot, then remove the pan from the heat and let it cool thoroughly before wiping it round inside with kitchen paper. The pan is now ready to use. After cooking omelettes in it, do not wash the pan – just wipe it clean with kitchen paper and then store until needed.

Or...

- You can make this with all sorts of vegetables, depending on what you like and what's in season. Try sliced chestnut or wild mushrooms, sliced red and yellow peppers, asparagus, diced potatoes (as in a Spanish omelette) or chopped baby spinach, rocket or watercress.
- If you're not vegetarian, try adding shredded leeks to the onion, and smoked salmon trimmings and chopped dill to the beaten eggs.

Pasta arrabbiata

Preparation: 5 minutes
Cooking: 30 minutes
Serves: 2
Per serving:
220 kcal
11g protein
35g carbs
5g fat

4 tablespoons vegetable stock **or** LighterLife Savoury Stock
1 small onion, chopped
2 garlic cloves, crushed
1 fresh red chilli, finely sliced
1 x 400g (14oz) can chopped tomatoes
1 tablespoon tomato purée
pinch of sugar
small bunch fresh basil, chopped
1 tablespoon capers
10 black olives, pitted
freshly ground black pepper
175g (6oz) penne or other pasta shapes (dry weight)
1 tablespoon grated or shaved Parmesan cheese

This favourite Roman pasta dish is usually made with penne (which means 'quills' or 'feathers' in Italian). The chunky tomato sauce, which complements the pasta tubes, derives its name from its hot, 'angry' flavour. In summer, when fresh tomatoes are ripe and plentiful, use 600g (1¼lb) instead of canned ones.

1 Heat the stock in a saucepan and add the onion, garlic and chilli. Cook gently until the onion is softened and golden.

2 Stir in the tomatoes, tomato purée, sugar, most of the chopped basil, capers and olives. Season with ground black pepper and simmer gently over a very low heat for 20–30 minutes, until the sauce is reduced to a thick consistency.

3 While the sauce is cooking, bring a large saucepan of water to the boil and throw in the pasta. Continue boiling for the time specified on the packet (usually 8–10 minutes), until the pasta is just tender but resists a little when you bite into it (*al dente*). Drain well in a colander.

4 Toss the cooked pasta with the arrabbiata sauce and divide between two serving plates or deep bowls. Sprinkle with the remaining basil and the Parmesan cheese. Serve immediately with a crisp salad.

Tip

This sauce tastes just as delicious tossed with cooked spaghetti, linguine or wider noodles, such as fettuccine.

Or...

- On a winter's evening, mix the cooked penne into the sauce, transfer to an ovenproof dish, dot the top with sliced low-fat mozzarella cheese and bake in a preheated oven at 180°C, gas mark 4 for 15 minutes, until the cheese has melted and the sauce is bubbling.
- For a more distinctive flavour, non-vegetarians can add 45g (1½oz) drained anchovy fillets.

Spinach-stuffed jacket potatoes

Preparation: 10 minutes
Cooking: 50 minutes
Serves: 2
Per serving:
92 kcal
6g protein
13g carbs
2g fat

2 medium baking potatoes, e.g.
Desirée, King Edward or Maris Piper
1 garlic clove, crushed
1 bag of fresh baby spinach leaves
1 large carrot, grated
3 tablespoons low-fat quark **or**
fromage frais
2 teaspoons grated Parmesan
cheese
freshly ground black pepper

Filled baked potatoes are an easy, versatile light meal. They're naturally fat-free, low in calories, and packed with nutrients, including vitamin C and fibre. Add your favourite topping – we've suggested some vegetarian ideas as well as this tasty, cheesy spinach.

1 Preheat the oven to 200°C, gas mark 6.

2 Prick the skin of each potato and then bake in the preheated oven for about 45 minutes, until soft and cooked. Alternatively, microwave each potato on high for approximately 8–10 minutes, until soft.

3 Meanwhile, put the garlic and 2 tablespoons water in a saucepan and heat gently for 2 minutes. Add the spinach and cook for 2 more minutes, until it turns bright green and wilts. Drain well in a colander, pressing down with a saucer to squeeze out any excess moisture.

4 Chop the spinach and mix in a bowl with the grated carrot, quark or fromage frais and 1 teaspoon grated Parmesan cheese.

5 Split the cooked potatoes in half and scoop out some of the cooked flesh, leaving a little around the edge. Stir the cooked potato into the spinach mixture and season to taste with black pepper.

6 Fill the potato shells with the spinach mixture, sprinkle with the remaining Parmesan and pop back into the hot oven for 5 minutes to warm through. Alternatively, microwave on high for 1 minute. Serve immediately with salad and broad beans or green vegetables.

Tip

If you're short on time but still like your potatoes to have a crispy skin, microwave as above and then place the potatoes in a hot preheated oven at 240°C, gas mark 9 for 10 minutes to finish.

Or...

Make delicious alternative fillings for baked potatoes. Try the ones below.
- Low-fat coleslaw mixed with grated apple and very low-fat natural cottage cheese.
- Virtually fat-free fromage frais mixed with chopped sun-dried tomatoes (without oil), spring onions, diced cucumber and chives.
- Roasted vegetables (diced courgette, peppers, aubergine and garlic) mixed into low-fat natural yoghurt.
- Reduced-sugar/salt baked beans topped with grated, reduced-fat Cheddar cheese.

Stuffed aubergine
with tzatziki

Preparation: 15 minutes
Cooking: 50 minutes
Serves: 2
Per serving:
259 kcal
11g protein
49g carbs
2g fat

250ml (9fl oz) stock made with
LighterLife Savoury Stock
100g (3½oz) couscous
2 medium aubergines
1 garlic clove, crushed
6 spring onions, chopped
3 ripe tomatoes, chopped
2 tablespoons lemon juice
2 tablespoons chopped parsley
1 teaspoon ground cumin
1 teaspoon chilli powder
½ teaspoon turmeric
freshly ground black pepper

Tzatziki
½ small cucumber, diced
5 tablespoons low-fat natural
yoghurt
2 spring onions, finely chopped
1 garlic clove, crushed
2 tablespoons chopped mint
grated zest of 1 lemon

Aubergine and couscous are a classic combination in Middle Eastern food. Don't be put off by the long list of ingredients – this delicious supper is easy to cook. Because it tastes equally good served cold, you can even prepare it well in advance and then cover and refrigerate it until you're ready to eat.

1 Preheat the oven to 190°C, gas mark 5.

2 Bring 200ml (7fl oz) of the stock to the boil and then pour over the couscous in a bowl. Cover and leave it to stand for at least 5 minutes before fluffing up with a fork.

3 Cut the stem off each aubergine and slice in half lengthways. With a sharp knife, remove most of the flesh and dice. Place the aubergine shells, skin-side down, in an ovenproof dish.

4 Put the remaining stock in a heavy-based saucepan, add the diced aubergine, garlic and spring onions, and cook gently until softened, stirring occasionally. Stir in the tomatoes and cook until softened. Add the lemon juice, parsley and spices, together with the cooked couscous. Mix well and season to taste with black pepper.

5 Fill each aubergine shell with the mixture, then cover with foil and bake in the preheated oven for 35–40 minutes, until cooked through.

6 While the aubergines are cooking, mix together the tzatziki ingredients in a small bowl, then cover and chill in the fridge until required.

7 Serve the stuffed aubergines hot, lukewarm or cold with the tzatziki and a crisp salad.

Tip

Many recipes advocate sprinkling the raw, cut aubergine with salt and then leaving it to exude any bitter juice before rinsing and cooking, but this takes time and is seldom worth the effort – most modern varieties tend not to be bitter.

Or...

● Instead of couscous, soak the same quantity of bulgar wheat in the stock and then mix with the other filling ingredients. Bulgar has a crunchy, more interesting texture.
● Chop the whole aubergines and cook as above, then use the cooked mixture as a filling for warm pitta breads.
● Serve with a traditional Greek salad of ripe tomatoes, cucumber, cos lettuce and diced low-fat feta cheese, tossed in an oil-free dressing.

Mushroom toads with red onion gravy

Preparation: 10 minutes
Standing: 5–10 minutes
Cooking: 20 minutes
Serves: 2
Per serving:
272 kcal
14g protein
33g carbs
7g fat

60g (2oz) plain flour
1 medium egg
150ml (¼ pint) skimmed milk
pinch of fresh thyme leaves
freshly ground black pepper
85g (3oz) button or chestnut
mushrooms, halved or quartered

Red onion gravy
1 medium red onion, thinly sliced
250ml (8fl oz) vegetable stock **or**
LighterLife Savoury Stock
1 dessertspoon plain flour
1 glass red wine
pinch of mustard powder
pinch of brown sugar
freshly ground black pepper

Here's a low-calorie vegetarian version of traditional toad in the hole. Flavoured with mushrooms and thyme, and served with a delicious red onion gravy, it's terrific for warming up on cold winter days.

1 Preheat the oven to 220°C, gas mark 7.

2 Sift the flour into a basin, add the egg and gradually beat in the skimmed milk, until you have a smooth batter with no lumps. Add the thyme leaves and black pepper. Set aside to stand for 5–10 minutes.

3 Place two shallow individual non-stick ovenproof dishes or two non-stick muffin pans on a baking tray and pop them into the preheated oven for about 5 minutes, until they're really hot.

4 Quickly pour in the batter and then add the mushrooms. Put them back in the oven straight away and cook for 20 minutes, or until the batter rises and the puddings are crisp and golden brown.

5 Meanwhile, make the gravy: put the onion in a pan with 3 tablespoons stock and cook gently over a low heat for 10 minutes, until tender and caramelized. Stir in the plain flour and then gradually add the rest of the stock with the red wine, stirring all the time with a wooden spoon. Flavour with mustard powder and the brown sugar, and season to taste with black pepper. If the gravy is too thick, just thin it with a little more stock or some cooking water from your vegetables. Simmer gently for 5 minutes.

6 Serve the mushroom toads immediately in a pool of red onion gravy with a selection of fresh vegetables.

Tip

Make life easier and take the hard work out of cooking by using an electric hand whisk to beat the batter to a really smooth consistency.

Or...

● You can use vegetarian sausages (e.g. Quorn) instead of mushrooms. Brown them first under a hot grill.
● Try adding other vegetables or vine fruits to the batter, such as halved cherry tomatoes or sliced peppers. Sweetcorn kernels work well, too.

106

Risotto primavera

Preparation: 15 minutes
Cooking: 25 minutes
Serves: 2
Per serving:
278 calories
12g protein
32g carbs
9g fat

300ml (½ pint) hot vegetable stock **or LighterLife Savoury Stock**
1 onion, finely chopped
1 garlic clove, crushed
115g (4oz) Arborio or risotto rice
½ glass dry or medium dry white wine (optional)
pinch of saffron (powdered or threads)
freshly ground black pepper
2 small courgettes, sliced
60g (2oz) baby asparagus
60g (2oz) shelled peas **or** mangetout
4 tablespoons chopped parsley
1 tablespooon low-fat crème fraîche
2 tablespoons coarsely grated Parmesan cheese
cherry tomatoes on the vine, to serve

In Italy, risotto is 'slow food' and you shouldn't try to hurry it along – this dish needs to be cooked very gently and slowly and will taste all the better for it. A perfect risotto should neither be soft and mushy nor crunchy – the rice should be comfortingly tender, moist and plump but still retaining a little 'bite'.

1 Heat 3 tablespoons stock in a heavy-based frying pan. Add the onion and garlic and cook over a low heat for 5 minutes, until softened.

2 Stir in the rice and cook for 1 minute, until the grains are glistening. Add the white wine (if using) and turn up the heat. Let the mixture bubble away until all the wine has evaporated.

3 Add a little of the remaining hot stock, together with the saffron and black pepper, and simmer gently, stirring occasionally, until all the liquid has been absorbed. Keep adding more stock in this way, a little at a time, until the rice is tender and creamy – this takes 15–20 minutes.

4 Meanwhile, cook the courgettes, asparagus and peas or mangetout in boiling water for 2–3 minutes. Drain well and stir gently into the risotto about 5 minutes before the end of cooking time. The vegetables will continue to cook in the heat of the rice.

5 Remove the pan from the heat and stir in the chopped parsley and crème fraîche. Season to taste with more black pepper. Sprinkle with Parmesan cheese and serve immediately with a crisp salad or some grilled cherry tomatoes on the vine.

Tips

- You need to use risotto rice for this recipe – basmati or long-grain rice won't work as they don't soften to the same tenderness and velvety texture.
- If fresh peas are out of season, add a handful of frozen ones instead. You can also flavour the risotto with chopped mint instead of parsley.

Or...

- Make a mushroom risotto with fresh chestnut or wild mushrooms or some dried porcini, which has been soaked first in boiling water. Cook the mushrooms with the onion and garlic before adding the rice.
- Other vegetables that work well in risotto include butternut squash, leeks, sweet peppers and plum tomatoes.
- If you're not a vegetarian, how about making a seafood risotto with prawns, scallops, mussels and squid – or use frozen fruits de mer.

Butternut squash and vegetable curry

Preparation: 15 minutes
Cooking: 25 minutes
Serves: 2
Per serving:
361 kcal
18g protein
59g carbs
8g fat

**300ml (½ pint) vegetable stock or
LighterLife Savoury Stock**

1 red onion, thinly sliced

2 large garlic cloves, crushed

**2 teaspoons each ground cumin,
coriander, turmeric, hot paprika
and chilli powder**

**1 small butternut squash, peeled
and cut into small chunks**

1 carrot, cut into matchsticks

**1 x 400g (14oz) can chickpeas,
rinsed and drained**

1 red pepper, deseeded and diced

½ small cauliflower, cut into florets

85g (3oz) brown basmati rice

few sprigs of coriander, chopped

pinch of ground cumin

freshly ground black pepper

**115ml (4fl oz) low-fat natural
yoghurt**

In this delicately scented curry, the butternut squash is flavoured with a selection of aromatic spices and cooked gently until tender. You can make this dish as hot or as mild as you wish. The spicy yoghurt accompaniment has an extremely cooling effect.

1 Put 2 tablespoons stock in a hot saucepan. Add the red onion, garlic and spices and heat gently, stirring well, for 5 minutes. Add the squash, carrot and chickpeas with 200ml (7fl oz) stock, and cook over a low heat for about 10 minutes, until the vegetables are just tender.

2 Add the red pepper and cauliflower with the rest of the stock and cook for another 10 minutes or so, until all the vegetables are tender.

3 Meanwhile, cook the brown rice in a saucepan with 200ml (7fl oz) boiling water for about 15 minutes or until tender. Drain well.

4 Spoon the rice on to two serving plates, top with the curry and garnish with chopped coriander.

5 Add a pinch of ground cumin and a grinding of black pepper to the yoghurt and serve with the curry.

Tip

To intensify the heat of the curry, use 4 teaspoons each of hot paprika and cayenne or chilli powder, and add 2 teaspoons garam masala.

Or...

● Vary the vegetables according to what you have available. Experiment with aubergine, yellow and green pepper, tomatoes, mushrooms, fresh root ginger and fresh chillies, until you find a combination of ingredients you like.
● Take the heat out of the curry and make it more soothing and creamy by stirring the yoghurt gently into the curry at the end of cooking.

Spiced Moroccan vegetable couscous

Preparation: 10 minutes
Standing: 5–10 minutes
Cooking: 30–40 minutes
Serves: 2
Per serving:
397 kcal
20g protein
71g carbs
5g fat

1 small onion, chopped
1 garlic clove, crushed
300ml (½ pint) vegetable stock **or**
LighterLife Savoury Stock
½ red or yellow pepper, deseeded
and cut into chunks
1 large carrot, cut into chunks
1 courgette, thickly sliced
1 red chilli, deseeded and sliced
(optional)
1 cinnamon stick
pinch each of ground nutmeg,
allspice, ginger, coriander
and cumin
pinch of saffron strands
1 x 200g (7oz) can chopped tomatoes
1 x 200g (7oz) can chickpeas,
drained and rinsed
freshly ground black pepper
115g (4oz) couscous
2 tablespoons chopped fresh
coriander **or** flat-leaf parsley
harissa paste, to serve (optional)

Cooked in the time-honoured way with the couscous gently steaming above the spicy vegetables and chickpeas, this is a low-fat version of a North African classic dish. If you like hot food, you could try adding a chopped fresh red chilli with the spices.

1 Put the onion and garlic in a large saucepan with a few spoonfuls of the stock and cook gently for about 5 minutes, until softened.

2 Add the red or yellow pepper, carrot, courgette and chilli (if using), and cook gently until just tender. Add the cinnamon stick, ground spices and saffron and stir well.

3 Stir in the tomatoes and chickpeas and add the remaining stock. Season with black pepper and simmer for 20–30 minutes, until the vegetables are cooked and the liquid has reduced and thickened.

4 About 10 minutes before the end of the cooking time, place the top section of a steamer or a colander lined with a clean kitchen cloth, thin tea towel or muslin square over the pan. Add the couscous, cover with a lid and steam for 10 minutes above the simmering vegetables, until the couscous is cooked.

5 Fluff up the couscous grains with a fork and divide between two serving plates. Add the vegetables (removing the cinnamon stick) and scatter with chopped herbs. Serve the harissa paste separately.

Tips

- You can buy harissa paste in tubes from most supermarkets as well as delicatessens. Use very sparingly as it's searingly hot!
- Instead of using different ground spices, you can obtain a Moroccan spice mix called ras-el-hanout, which combines them all. It's available from Middle Eastern stores and some supermarkets.

Or...

- Change the vegetables according to what's available – try pumpkin, butternut squash, sweet potato, turnip, aubergine or parsnips.
- Serve the couscous with some cooling plain low-fat natural yoghurt.

Veggie beanburgers with salsa

Preparation: 15 minutes
Cooking: 30 minutes
Serves: 2
Per serving:
151 kcal
8g protein
29g carbs
2g fat

2 tablespoons vegetable stock **or**
LighterLife Savoury Stock
½ onion, finely chopped
1 carrot, grated
½ red pepper, deseeded and
finely chopped
1 garlic clove, crushed
½ teaspoon ground coriander
½ teaspoon chilli powder
1 x 200g (7oz) can red kidney beans,
drained and rinsed
60g (2oz) soft white breadcrumbs
2 tablespoons chopped coriander
freshly ground black pepper
60g (2oz) dried wholewheat
breadcrumbs
2 dessertspoons hot salsa
(see page 138)
2 tablespoons virtually fat-free
plain fromage frais
lime wedges, to garnish

These spicy veggie burgers are simple to make and very filling. We have served them with salsa but you could try topping them with some low-fat guacamole, Thai sweet chilli sauce or even some old-fashioned tomato ketchup – whatever takes your fancy.

1 Preheat the oven to 200°C, gas mark 6.

2 Heat the stock in a saucepan over a medium heat. When hot, add the onion, then cover and cook gently for 5 minutes, stirring occasionally. Add the carrot, red pepper and garlic and cook for a further 5 minutes. Add the coriander and chilli powder and stir for 2 minutes, then remove the pan from the heat.

3 Mash the drained kidney beans in a bowl and mix in the fresh white breadcrumbs and chopped coriander. Add the onion mixture, mix well and season with black pepper.

4 Divide the kidney bean mixture into four equal-sized portions and, using your hands, shape into burgers and coat lightly with the dried wholewheat breadcrumbs (see page 32).

5 Place the burgers on non-stick greaseproof paper on a baking tray and bake in the preheated oven for about 10 minutes, until crisp and golden brown on one side, then turn them over and brown the other side.

6 Serve the hot burgers with a spoonful of hot salsa and some fromage frais. Eat with a crisp mixed salad and serve with lime wedges.

Tips

- Instead of oven-baking the burgers, you can cook them under a preheated grill or even over hot coals on a barbecue.
- If you don't have any dried breadcrumbs, simply dust the burgers lightly with flour before grilling.

Or...

Vary the flavours by using different canned beans in this recipe. Choose from chickpeas, butter beans or haricot beans. Just drain and mash with the other ingredients in the same way.

success story

Diane
lost six dress sizes in five months

Diane
Dress size then: 22
Dress size now: 10

" *My job as a cake baker meant that I had the perfect excuse to overeat. I could easily get through several cupcakes' worth of batter while preparing ingredients. I was forever scraping the mixing bowls clean with a spoon. I found it soothing because it brought back memories of cleaning the bowl when my mother used to bake. I was worried I'd never kick the habit. But, once I joined LighterLife, my LighterLife Weight-Management Counsellor said to me: 'Why do you need to be a slave to that behaviour?'*

Another unhealthy habit was chocolate. On top of that, I was always baking fattening things for the family at home – cakes, scones and delicious bread. Even my savoury dishes were high in calories – I cooked lots of pasta with creamy sauces.

My weight had been an issue all my adult life but I'd tried various diets and always put the weight back on fairly quickly. It was quite depressing and I knew something fundamentally had to change.

I found out about LighterLife because a friend had lost a lot of weight on the programme. Another catalyst for signing up was realising that if I didn't lose weight I'd never enjoy dancing in public again. As a child and teenager, I used to do ballet and I loved it, but once I started piling on the pounds I felt too embarrassed to continue. LighterLife Total gave me clear boundaries about what I could and couldn't eat or drink and I liked that. I couldn't cut corners. I was delighted to be one of the fastest losers in my group, dropping nine pounds in the blink of an eye, and the programme delivered everything it said it would.

To my mind, what makes LighterLife unique is the support and group work, which really helped me to look at the psychological reasons why I ate so much, so I could change from the inside out. I love the tools, such as the food and mood diary. And I enjoyed sharing my journey with the other women in the group. In the past, I'd been on other weight-loss plans that held weekly meetings but none were a patch on the LighterLife groups, which went much deeper.

My number-one tip for long-term success is to keep coming to the groups even after you reach your desired weight. I've long since reached a healthy BMI but I still go to a Management group every week. I spent years battling weight problems and don't want to return to unhealthy eating. I don't feel like I have to cope alone and so food is no longer a big issue for me. I've stopped baking loads of goodies for the family and eat a balanced diet. I haven't cut anything out.

Best of all, I recently joined a female dance group and I really love the opportunity to dance in public and wear sparkly costumes. ,,

Diane, now a size 10

www.lighterlife.com

sweet

Summer fruit stacks

Preparation: 20 minutes
Cooking: 10 minutes
Serves: 2
Per serving:
155 kcal
10g protein
22g carbs
3g fat

2 x 15g (½oz) sheets filo pastry
1 small egg, beaten
2 ripe apricots
60g (2oz) ripe cherries
60g (2oz) raspberries
100g (3½oz) 0% fat Greek yoghurt
icing sugar, for dusting
sprigs of mint, to decorate

Stylish and elegant, this delicious dessert is simplicity itself to make. Keep a roll of ready-made filo pastry in your freezer ready to defrost and use as required. If you're entertaining friends, you could double the ingredients to make one long rectangular stack and then cut it into slices to serve.

1 Preheat the oven to 200°F, gas mark 6.

2 Cut the two sheets of filo pastry in half, so you have four squares. Place one sheet on a clean work surface and brush lightly with beaten egg. Place another sheet on top and brush with egg. Continue layering all four sheets in this way, brushing with egg between them.

3 Brush the top with beaten egg and then cut the filo pastry square in half into two rectangles. Cut each rectangular strip into three equal-sized squares. You should end up with six squares.

4 Place the filo squares on a non-stick baking tray and bake in the preheated oven for 8–10 minutes, until they're crisp and lightly golden brown. Remove and cool.

5 Prepare the fruit: quarter the apricots, removing the stones; pit the cherries; and check that the raspberries are unblemished.

6 When thoroughly cool, spread a little of the yoghurt over one of the filo squares. Top with two apricot quarters, some cherries and raspberries, and cover with another filo square. Spread with more yoghurt and add two quartered apricots, cherries and raspberries, and then top with a third filo sheet. Assemble the other stack in the same way, reserving a few raspberries and/or cherries for decoration.

7 Place each stack on a serving plate, surround with the remaining fruit and then dust lightly with icing sugar. Serve immediately, decorated with sprigs of mint.

Tip

You can bake the filo squares a day in advance and store them in an airtight container until you're ready to assemble and serve the stacks.

Or...

- Use other summer fruits, such as quartered or sliced peaches with redcurrants or strawberries.
- In winter, assemble the stacks with sliced mango or papaya, clementine segments and kiwi fruit, and decorate with physallis.

Poached spiced pears

Preparation: 10 minutes
Cooking: 30 minutes
Serves: 2
Per serving:
126 kcal
1g protein
26g carbs
2g fat

150ml (¼ pint) pomegranate juice
60ml (2fl oz) cranberry juice
juice and grated zest of 1 orange
1 cinnamon stick
½ teaspoon grated nutmeg
1 tablespoon runny honey
2 ripe but firm pears
2 dessertspoons virtually fat-free fromage frais
slivers of orange zest, to decorate

Although you can enjoy this dessert all year round, it's perfect in the autumn when fresh pears are cheap and plentiful. Easy to make, it can be enjoyed hot or cold – just cool thoroughly and then leave in a covered container in the fridge until required.

1 Put the pomegranate, cranberry and orange juices in a large saucepan with the orange zest, spices and honey, and then warm through gently over a low heat.

2 Peel each pear, leaving the stem intact, and remove the core from the base, using a small knife or corer. Slice a small section off the bottom of each pear to enable them to stand up on their own.

3 Place the pears upright in the pan and baste with the warm juice and spice mixture. Simmer gently for 20–30 minutes, until cooked. The pears should be tender when pierced with the point of a knife. Remove them from the pan and transfer to two serving plates.

4 Turn up the heat and let the juice bubble away until it has reduced by half and has become syrupy. Remove the cinnamon stick.

5 To serve, spoon the syrup over the top of each pear. Serve warm with a spoonful of fromage frais and some thin slivers of orange zest.

Tip

Use perfect juicy pears, which are not bruised or misshapen. Sturdy Williams or Comice are better than Conference pears for this dessert, and they will stand up more easily.

Or...

You can poach other orchard fruits in the same way – plums and greengages are especially good simmered in orange juice with whole cloves and a cinnamon stick. You could also try adding a little red wine to the poaching liquid.

Strawberry meringue

Preparation: 15 minutes
Cooking: 1 hour plus cooling
Serves: 2
Per serving:
133 kcal
14g protein
17g carbs
1g fat

2 medium egg whites

¼ teaspoon cream of tartar

2 tablespoons icing sugar plus a little for dusting

250g (9oz) quark or virtually fat-free fromage frais

250g (9oz) ripe strawberries, sliced

sprigs of mint, to decorate

This classic summer dessert looks and tastes fabulous. The meringue is not as crisp as a traditional pavlova as less sugar is used, but the slightly soft, chewy texture is delicious and makes a lovely contrast to the creamy quark and fresh strawberries. If you don't have time to make the meringue, you can buy ready-made meringue nests in the supermarket and top them with quark and fruit in the same way, although this will increase the calorie/carb content.

1 Preheat the oven to 120°C, gas mark ½.

2 Line a baking tray with non-stick greaseproof paper or edible rice paper. Draw two circles round two saucers on to the parchment.

3 Put the egg whites in a spotlessly clean metal or glass bowl. Beat them with an electric mixer or a hand whisk until foamy. Add the cream of tartar, then whisk again until soft peaks are formed. Add the icing sugar, one tablespoon at a time, beating at high speed between each addition. Continue whisking until the egg whites are stiff and glossy.

4 Spoon the meringue mixture onto the paper to fill the circles you've drawn and form a bowl shape, with the edges thicker than the middle.

5 Cook in the preheated oven for 1 hour, then switch off the oven but leave the meringue inside to continue cooking slowly until the oven is cold. Remove and allow to cool completely.

6 Ease the meringue away from the baking paper (it doesn't matter if it breaks). If you used rice paper, there's no need to remove it.

7 When you're ready to serve, place the meringue on a serving plate and cover with the Quark or fromage frais, spreading it over the base. Pile the strawberries up in a mound on top and dust lightly with icing sugar. Serve immediately, decorated with sprigs of mint.

Tip

The meringue base can be made a day or two in advance if it's kept in an airtight container.

Or...

- Top the cooled meringue base with low-fat plain or fruity yoghurt instead of quark or fromage frais.
- Try using different fruit or a mixture to vary the colours and flavours. Choose from soft berry fruits, such as raspberries, blackberries and blueberries, or diced peaches, plums, mango or kiwi fruit.

Mango and raspberry sorbets with coulis

Preparation: 15 minutes
Freezing: 24 hours
Serves: 2
Per serving:
109 kcal
2g protein
23g carbs
1g fat

1 ripe mango
115g (4oz) raspberries
1 tablespoon icing sugar
juice of 1 orange
½ tablespoon Cointreau (optional)
fresh berries (redcurrants, strawberries, raspberries), to decorate
sprigs of mint, to decorate

Fresh fruit coulis
60g (2oz) fresh soft fruits, e.g. strawberries, redcurrants
1 teaspoon lemon juice
1 teaspoon icing sugar

The great thing about sorbets is that not only are they very healthy and low in calories and fat but they can also be made in advance and then frozen until needed. This duet looks very elegant if you're are entertaining.

1 With a sharp knife, cut down through the mango on either side of the stone. Remove the peel and chop the flesh. Place the diced mango in a freezer-proof container and freeze for at least 24 hours.

2 Make the raspberry sorbet: crush the raspberries with a fork and press through a sieve. Sweeten the raspberry juice with icing sugar and pour into a freezer-proof container. Freeze for at least 24 hours.

3 Make the fruit coulis by blending the soft fruits in a food processor or blender and then stirring in the lemon juice and icing sugar.

4 Place the frozen mango, orange juice and Cointreau (optional) in a food processor or blender and blitz until smooth.

5 Put a scoop of each fruit sorbet on two dessert plates. Pour a little of the fruit coulis around them and decorate with fresh berries and sprigs of mint. Serve immediately.

Tips

- For a smoother fruit coulis, just press the fruit through a sieve to remove any pips before sweetening and adding the lemon juice.
- If wished, you can beat the frozen fruit mixtures with a hand whisk to break up the ice crystals and then refreeze before serving.

Or...

Experiment with different fruit – try papaya instead of mango, and substitute strawberries for the raspberries. In the autumn or winter, you could use blackberries or blueberries.

Peach and blueberry brûlées

Preparation: 10 minutes
Chilling: 30 minutes
Cooking: 2–3 minutes
Serves: 2
Per serving:
89 kcal
4g protein
16g carbs
1g fat

2 ripe peaches
85g (3oz) blueberries
grated zest of 1 small orange
150ml (5fl oz) thick low-fat natural yoghurt
2 teaspoons Demerara sugar

This is such an easy dessert to make – and it looks and tastes fabulous. A healthier version of the traditional crème brûlée, which is made with double cream, this is lighter and less cloying, so you don't have to worry about counting the calories.

1 Cut the peaches in half, remove the stones and skin, and then cut the flesh into slices or chunks. Divide them between two individual shallow flameproof dishes or ramekins. Mix the blueberries in with the peaches and then grate the orange zest over the top.

2 Cover the fruit with the yoghurt, using a palette knife or spoon to smooth and level the tops. Transfer to the refrigerator and chill for at least 30 minutes.

3 When you're ready to caramelize the brûlées, preheat the grill until it's really hot. Sprinkle the sugar evenly over the top of the yoghurt to cover it thinly and then place the dishes under the hot grill, watching and turning them, so the sugar melts evenly. As soon as it turns golden brown and starts to caramelize, remove the dishes before the caramel burns. (You could use a cook's blow torch instead for this step.)

4 Set aside to cool before serving, so the topping is hard and crisp. If wished, pop them back in the refrigerator until required.

Tips

- Always thoroughly chill the yoghurt by placing the desserts in the fridge for a while before sprinkling with sugar and caramelizing.
- Do allow the caramel to cool before eating.
- If you don't have Demerara, caster, golden caster or granulated sugar will work instead.

Or...

- Depending on the time of year and which fruits are available, try making this dessert with one or a combination of the following: raspberries, strawberries, redcurrants, grapes, sliced banana, kiwi, mango and nectarines.
- Try covering the fruit with 0% fat Greek yoghurt, which keeps its shape beautifully and tastes delicious, with a pleasantly creamy texture.

Baked apples with blackberries

Preparation: 10 minutes
Cooking: 30 minutes
Serves: 2
Per serving:
77 kcal
16g carbs
1g fat

2 large cooking apples, e.g. Bramleys
150g (5oz) blackberries
2 teaspoons runny honey
juice of 1 lemon
grated zest and juice of 1 orange
2 x 30ml (1fl oz) scoops reduced-fat vanilla ice cream or virtually fat-free fromage frais

This is a great autumnal pudding when apples and blackberries are in season and cheap and plentiful. Why not get some exercise by going for a walk in the countryside and picking wild blackberries in the hedgerows? If you can't get hold of any fresh berries, you could use frozen ones instead.

1 Preheat the oven to 190°C, gas mark 5.

2 Core the apples and, with a sharp knife, make a shallow cut through the skin horizontally around the middle of each one.

3 Place the apples in a non-stick baking dish and fill the hollowed-out centres with most of the blackberries. Scatter any remaining berries around them. Drizzle a spoonful of honey over each apple and sprinkle with lemon and orange juice and the orange zest.

4 Bake in the preheated oven for about 30 minutes, until the apples are soft and cooked through but have not lost their shape. Baste them occasionally during cooking with the pan juices to keep them moist.

5 With a slice, carefully transfer the baked apples to two serving dishes and then pour over any pan juices and loose blackberries. Serve with a scoop of reduced-fat vanilla ice cream or fromage frais.

Tip

Scoring the apples around the middle before cooking will help them to keep their shape and cook right through more evenly. If you don't do this, they may be tough and fibrous in the centre after cooking.

Or...

- Fill the apples in summer with soft berries, such as blackcurrants, redcurrants and blueberries. In winter, make a filling of chopped dried exotic fruits, apricots and dates.
- To make a fruit filling more interesting, add chopped nuts, crumbled amaretti biscuits or a pinch of ground cinnamon or nutmeg.
- Instead of ice cream, serve the apples with virtually fat-free fromage frais or some low-fat, natural yoghurt.

Summer baked spiced peaches

Preparation: 5 minutes
Cooking: 15–20 minutes
Serves: 2
Per serving:
65 kcal
3g protein
11g carbs
1g fat

2 fresh ripe peaches, halved and stones removed

2 teaspoons Demerara sugar

pinch of ground cinnamon or nutmeg

juice of ½ lemon

4 tablespoons quark, virtually fat-free fromage frais or 0% fat Greek yoghurt

summer berries (redcurrants, raspberries or strawberries), to garnish

Always use ripe peaches when you are making this dessert. The stones will be easier to remove and the fruit will be more juicy and succulent. If you don't have any peaches, you could prepare and cook fresh apricots, greengages or plums in the same way.

1 Preheat the oven to 200°C, gas mark 6.

2 Cut each peach in half and ease out the stone. Place the peaches, cut-side up, on a non-stick baking sheet. Sprinkle them with a little Demerara sugar, cinnamon or nutmeg and a few drops of lemon juice.

3 Bake the peaches in the preheated oven for 15–20 minutes, until tender and golden brown on top.

4 Serve the peaches warm, topped with a spoonful of quark, fromage frais or Greek yoghurt, with a few summer berries as a garnish.

Tip

You can use any sugar in this recipe but Demerara tastes best and browns particularly well.

Or...

- Use nectarines instead of peaches and sprinkle with 1 tablespoon orange liqueur before baking in the oven.
- Sprinkle the peaches with 2 teaspoons diced stem ginger before cooking them as above.
- For an extra-special Italian twist on this recipe, mix three crushed amaretti biscuits with the quark or fromage frais and 1 teaspoon caster sugar, then pile into the peach halves, sprinkle with Amaretto liqueur and pop under a hot grill until bubbling and golden.

Quick and easy trifle

Preparation: 20 minutes
Chilling: 1 hour
Cooking: 10 minutes
Serves: 2
Per serving:
188 kcal
9g protein
29g carbs
4g fat

1 sachet sugar-free strawberry **or** raspberry jelly

115g (4oz) fresh berries, e.g. strawberries, raspberries, blueberries, pitted cherries **or** redcurrants

1 large ripe peach or nectarine

100g (3½oz) low-fat ready-made custard

150g (5oz) very low-fat vanilla yoghurt

2 amaretti biscuits, crumbled

2 small squares plain chocolate, coarsely grated

This fabulous recipe is much healthier and lower in calories than most other trifles and it's really simple to make, too. Prepare it in advance and then cover and chill in the fridge until you're ready to eat it.

1 Make up the sugar-free jelly according to the instructions on the packet.

2 Divide the berries between two glass sundae dishes or put them all in the bottom of a larger glass bowl. Pour the liquid jelly over the top of the berries and chill in the refrigerator until set firm.

3 Cut the peach or nectarine in half and remove the stone. Cut into thin slices and arrange over the top of the set jelly.

4 Pour the low-fat custard over the top to cover the peach, and then top with the vanilla yoghurt. Chill in the refrigerator until required.

5 Before serving, decorate the trifle(s) with the crumbled amaretti biscuits and grated chocolate.

Tip

You can buy ready-made custard in the chilled cabinets of most big supermarkets. However, do check the label to make sure that you're buying a low-calorie, low-fat product.

Or...

- Instead of sliced peach, use a more traditional sliced banana. Sprinkle with lemon juice to prevent it discolouring.
- Use low-fat fruit yoghurt instead of vanilla – strawberry, raspberry or apricot will all taste delicious and add colour.

basic recipes

Sauces and dips

Tomato sauce for pasta

Preparation: **5 minutes** Cooking: **35 minutes**
Serves: **2** Per serving: **62 kcal   3g protein**
12g carbs   0.6g fat

1 small onion, finely chopped
1 garlic clove, crushed
150ml (¼ pint) vegetable stock or LighterLife
Savoury Stock
1 x 400g (14oz) can chopped tomatoes
pinch of sugar
a few basil leaves, torn
1 teaspoon balsamic vinegar
freshly ground black pepper

1 Put the onion, garlic and stock in a pan and bring to the
boil. Cover the pan and continue boiling for 5 minutes,
then uncover and simmer gently for 15 minutes, or until
the liquid reduces and the onion is softened and golden.
2 Stir in the tomatoes, sugar and black pepper. Simmer
for 10 minutes, until the sauce is reduced and pulpy.
3 Add the fresh basil and balsamic vinegar and cook for
1 minute. Use in pasta dishes.

White sauce

Preparation: **2 minutes** Cooking: **5 minutes**
Serves: **2** Per serving: **102 kcal   11g protein**
15g carbs   0.4g fat

2 tablespoons cornflour
300ml (½ pint) skimmed milk
150ml (5fl oz) virtually fat-free fromage frais
good pinch of ground nutmeg
freshly ground black pepper

1 In a small bowl, blend the cornflour with a little of the
milk until the mixture is smooth and free from lumps.
2 Heat the remaining milk in a small saucepan. Just
before it boils, stir in the cornflour mixture and cook,
stirring all the time, over a gentle heat until the sauce
thickens – this takes 2–3 minutes.
3 Remove from the heat. Beat in the fromage frais and
season with nutmeg and black pepper. Use for lasagne,
moussaka, cauliflower cheese and pasta bakes.

Mexican salsa

Preparation: **10 minutes**
Serves: **2** Per serving: **77 kcal   3g protein**
13g carbs   0.9g fat

1 small red onion, finely chopped
1 fresh red chilli, finely chopped
½ red pepper, deseeded and chopped
225g (8oz) ripe red tomatoes (or canned chopped
tomatoes)
juice of ½ lime
2 tablespoons chopped fresh coriander
freshly ground black pepper

1 Mix together the chopped red onion, chilli and red
pepper in a bowl.
2 Chop the tomatoes finely or roughly. If you like, you
can remove the skins first by immersing them briefly
in boiling water, then peeling with your fingers.
3 Stir the chopped tomatoes into the onion, chilli and
pepper mixture. Mix in the lime juice and coriander,
and season to taste with black pepper.
4 Serve immediately or chill in the fridge until required.

Guacamole

Preparation: **10 minutes** Chilling: **30 minutes**
Serves: **2** Per serving: **119 kcal   3g protein**
9g carbs   8g fat

1 small ripe avocado
juice of 1 lime or ½ lemon
1 garlic clove, crushed
3 spring onions, finely chopped
1 fresh red or green chilli, deseeded and chopped
2 tablespoons chopped fresh coriander
2 ripe red tomatoes, skinned and chopped
freshly ground black pepper

1 Cut the avocado in half and remove the stone. Scoop
out the flesh and put in a bowl with the lime or lemon
juice. Mash the avocado coarsely with a fork or potato
masher.
2 Mix in the garlic, spring onions, chilli, coriander and
tomatoes. Season to taste with black pepper.
3 Cover the bowl and chill for at least 30 minutes before
serving as a dip or sauce with Mexican or grilled food.

Dressings and marinades

Oriental salad dressing

Preparation: **5 minutes**
Serves: **2** Per serving: **26 kcal   1g protein**
5g carbs   0.1g fat

2 tablespoons light soy sauce
juice of 1 lime
1 teaspoon rice or wine vinegar
1 red chilli, deseeded and finely chopped
1 garlic clove, crushed
1 teaspoon grated fresh root ginger
pinch of caster sugar
few fresh coriander leaves, chopped (optional)

1 In a bowl, mix together the soy sauce, lime juice and
rice or wine vinegar.
2 Stir in the chopped chilli, garlic and ginger, and then
mix in the sugar until you have a smooth, well-blended
dressing. If wished, add the chopped coriander.
3 Use to dress a salad, or store in a covered container
or screwtop jar in the fridge until required.

Teriyaki marinade

Preparation: **5 minutes**
Serves: **2** Per serving: **26 kcal   1g protein**
4g carbs   trace fat

2 tablespoons Japanese teriyaki sauce or dark
soy sauce
1 tablespoon sweet rice wine or sherry
1 teaspoon runny honey
1 garlic clove, crushed
juice and grated zest of 1 small orange

1 Measure the teriyaki or dark soy sauce into a basin
or shallow dish. Add the sweet rice wine or sherry and
honey and blend well.
2 Stir in the garlic together with the orange juice and
grated zest. Stir well and then use as a marinade for
chicken, pork or fish.

Honey mustard dressing

Preparation: **5 minutes**
Serves: **2** Per serving: **21 kcal   0.4g protein**
4g carbs   0.5g fat

2 tablespoons oil-free vinaigrette or French dressing
1 teaspoon cider vinegar
juice of ½ lemon
1 level teaspoon honey mustard
1 level teaspoon wholegrain mustard
1 teaspoon runny honey
freshly ground black pepper

1 Measure the oil-free dressing and cider vinegar into
a basin or a screwtop jar. Squeeze in the lemon juice.
2 Stir in the honey mustard and wholegrain mustard,
and then blend in the honey until you have a thick,
smooth, well-amalgamated dressing. If using a screwtop
jar, just seal with the lid and then shake vigorously.
3 Season with black pepper and use immediately,
or store in the fridge until needed.

Garlicky lemon and herb marinade

Preparation: **5 minutes**
Serves: **2** Per serving: **4 kcal   0.2g protein**
0.6g carbs   trace fat

juice of 1 large lemon
1 large garlic clove, crushed
1 tablespoon snipped chives
1 tablespoon finely chopped dill
1 tablespoon finely chopped parsley or coriander
freshly ground black pepper

1 Squeeze the lemon juice into a bowl and mix in the
garlic. Add the chives, dill and parsley or coriander.
2 Season with black pepper and use as a marinade
for white fish, chicken, lamb or grilled vegetables.
3 This marinade can be made in advance and stored
in the fridge in a sealed container until required.

Vegetable side dishes and salads

Baked spicy sweet potatoes

Preparation: **10 minutes** Cooking: **30–40 minutes**
Serves: **2** Per serving: **85 kcal   2g protein**
20g carbs   0.4g fat

2 x 175g (6oz) sweet potatoes, peeled
2 tablespoons low-fat plain yoghurt
1 garlic clove, crushed
squeeze of lemon juice
½ teaspoon each ground coriander and cumin
pinch each of chilli powder and turmeric
freshly ground black pepper

1 Preheat the oven to 200°C, gas mark 6.
2 Cut each sweet potato in half and then slice each half
lengthways into 3 wedges.
3 Mix together the yoghurt, garlic, lemon juice and spices.
Brush over the sweet potato wedges and arrange them
on a non-stick baking tray.
4 Bake in the preheated oven for 30–40 minutes, until
crisp, golden brown and tender.
5 Serve hot sprinkled with some ground black pepper.

Spring vegetables with grainy mustard dressing

Preparation: **5 minutes** Cooking: **10–15 minutes**
Serves: **2** Per serving: **75 kcal   5g protein**
11g carbs   1g fat

8 baby carrots, scraped
115g (4oz) thin green beans, topped and tailed
1 small broccoli head, cut into small florets
4 baby leeks, halved or quartered
1 tablespoon oil-free vinaigrette or French dressing
1 dessertspoon wholegrain mustard
dash of balsamic vinegar
squeeze of lemon juice
freshly ground black pepper

1 Put the vegetables in a colander or a steamer basket.
2 Place over a pan of boiling water and cover with a lid.
3 Steam for 10–15 minutes, until the vegetables are tender.
4 Mix together the oil-free dressing, mustard, balsamic
vinegar and lemon juice, until well amalgamated.
5 Toss the steamed vegetables lightly in the dressing.
Season with black pepper and serve hot.

Steamed seedy greens

Preparation: **5 minutes** Cooking: **5–10 minutes**
Serves: **2** Per serving: **70 kcal   7g protein**
3g carbs   6g fat

4 pak choi or 225g (8oz) spring greens or purple
sprouting broccoli
1 tablespoon pumpkin seeds
1 tablespoon sunflower seeds
1 teaspoon sesame seeds
1 tablespoon oyster sauce
few drops of sweet chilli sauce (to taste)
freshly ground black pepper

1 Wash the greens, checking for dirt and insects. Shake
or pat dry and place in a colander or steamer basket.
2 Fill a large saucepan with water and bring to the boil.
Place the colander or basket on top and cover with a lid.
3 Steam for 5–10 minutes, until the greens are cooked
and tender. Make sure it doesn't boil dry.
4 Meanwhile, put a small non-stick frying pan over a low
heat and add the seeds. Gently shake the pan and move
it around until the seeds turn pale golden brown.
5 Toss the greens in the oyster and chilli sauces and
sprinkle with the toasted seeds. Eat immediately.

Tangy green beans

Preparation: **5 minutes** Cooking: **20–30 minutes**
Serves: **2** Per serving: **97 kcal   6g protein**
16g carbs   1g fat

1 x 400g (14oz) carton passata (or 1 x 400g (14oz) can
tomatoes blitzed in a blender)
2 tablespoons balsamic or red wine vinegar
few shakes of Worcestershire sauce
1 teaspoon brown sugar
450g (1lb) thin green beans, topped and tailed

1 Mix the passata, vinegar, Worcestershire sauce
and brown sugar in a saucepan and gently bring to
a simmer.
2 Add the beans and cook gently for 15 minutes, or
until they are tender and the tomato sauce has reduced.
3 Alternatively, after adding the beans, transfer to an
ovenproof dish, loosely cover with foil and bake in a
preheated oven at 180°C, gas mark 4 for 30 minutes,
or until the beans are tender.

Herby new potato salad

Preparation: **10 minutes** Cooking: **10 minutes**
Serves: **2** Per serving: **84 kcal   2g protein**
18g carbs   0.5g fat

200g (7oz) baby new potatoes, scrubbed
4 spring onions, finely sliced
few sprigs of mint, chopped
2 tablespoons snipped chives
2 tablespoons finely chopped parsley
juice of ½ lemon
2 tablespoons oil-free vinaigrette or French dressing
½ teaspoon Dijon mustard
freshly ground black pepper

1 Cook the new potatoes in boiling water for 10 minutes, or until tender. Drain well.
2 Put the potatoes in a bowl with the spring onions and chopped herbs.
3 Whisk together the lemon juice, vinaigrette or French dressing and mustard until well combined.
4 Pour the dressing over the warm potatoes and toss gently. Grind some black pepper over the top and serve.

Hummus

Preparation: 5 minutes
Serves: **2** Per serving: **233 kcal   15g protein**
33g carbs   6g fat

1 x 400g (14oz) can chickpeas, drained and rinsed
juice of ½ lemon
1 garlic clove, crushed
1 teaspoon ground cumin
1 teaspoon ground coriander
2 tablespoons chopped parsley or fresh coriander
freshly ground black pepper

1 Put the chickpeas in a blender with the lemon juice, garlic, ground spices and herbs. Blitz until you have a thick, sludgy purée. If it's too thick for your liking, you can thin it with a little water or some more lemon juice.
2 Season with black pepper and spoon into a bowl. Eat immediately or cover and chill until required. Serve as a side dish to grilled fish, chicken and meat, or as a dip.

Balsamic grilled tomatoes and peppers

Preparation: **5 minutes** Cooking: **10–15 minutes**
Serves: **2** Per serving: **41 kcal   2g protein**
7g carbs   0.7g fat

1 red pepper
1 yellow pepper
1 green pepper
2 stems cherry tomatoes on the vine
1 tablespoon balsamic vinegar
freshly ground black pepper

1 Preheat the grill until it's very hot. Put the peppers on the grill pan and grill for 5–10 minutes, turning often, until blistered and slightly charred all over. Cool.
2 Put the tomatoes under the hot grill and cook for 4–5 minutes, until softened and slightly charred.
3 Peel the peppers, then cut them in half and discard the stems, seeds and ribs. Cut the flesh into large pieces.
4 Sprinkle the balsamic vinegar over the peppers and tomatoes. Add black pepper and serve lukewarm or cold.

Four bean salad

Preparation: **5 minutes** Cooking: **6 minutes**
Serves: **2** Per serving: **137 kcal   10g protein**
21g carbs   2g fat

85g (3oz) thin green beans, trimmed
85g (3oz) canned chickpeas, drained and rinsed
85g (3oz) canned red kidney beans, drained and rinsed
85g (3oz) canned butter beans, drained and rinsed
juice of ½ lemon
1 teaspoon balsamic or cider vinegar
freshly ground black pepper
2 tablespoons chopped parsley

1 Cook the green beans in a pan of boiling water for 5–6 minutes, until just tender. Drain and refresh in cold water.
2 Put all the canned beans in a bowl and add the cooled green beans.
3 Whisk the lemon juice and vinegar and sprinkle over the beans. Toss gently, season to taste with black pepper, and sprinkle with parsley.

index

Safe, simple, sustainable:
LighterLife is far more than a diet

Hundreds of thousands of people have successfully lost weight with LighterLife. If you're one stone or more overweight, you too could be living a lighter, healthier, more active life.

Unlike other weight-loss programmes, at LighterLife we know weight management is not just about what's going into your mouth: we help you understand what's going on in your head, so that you can improve both your lifestyle and your relationship with food.

We kick-start your weight loss with easy-to-use food replacements, then when you achieve your weight-loss goals we help you create a healthy, balanced and enjoyable eating plan that really works for you – including the tasty, no-added-fat recipes in this book!

And we also help you develop the skills to manage your weight successfully at our unique weekly group meetings, where you explore the reasons why you've used food in the past in the ways you have, and how in the future you can live more effectively than ever before, by making simple but powerful changes to the way you think, eat and live.

So, if you're ready for a weight-loss programme with a difference that's really committed to supporting you every step of the way, find your local Weight-Management Counsellor and contact them to start living lighter – not just for a couple of months or even a year or two, but for life.

LighterLife's programmes

- If you have at least three stone to lose – that's a body mass index (BMI) of 30 or more – you can join LighterLife Total. It's a very-low-calorie diet (VLCD) where, instead of conventional food, you have four of our nutritionally complete Foodpacks every day so you can lose weight quickly and safely.
- If you have one to three stone to lose – a BMI of 25-29.9 – you can join LighterLife Lite. This is a low-calorie diet (LCD), where you have three Foodpacks each day, and a meal from a selection of everyday, healthy foods.
- Whichever programme you're on, when you reach your desired weight, we help you reintroduce a full range of conventional food without putting the weight back on – and then, with the support of our free Management programme, we'll help you live lighter for life!

---

t UK 0800 2 988 988
ROI 1800 927 213

e inform@lighterlife.com

w www.lighterlife.com
www.lighterlifeformen.com

One year's FREE Subscription to the LighterLife Magazine

If you join LighterLife, or you're an exising client, simply complete and return this coupon to us at the address below, and receive an annual subscription* to our fantastic client magazine, LighterLife.

Name: _____

LighterLife Membership number: _____
(If you don't know this, please contact your Weight-Management Counsellor)

Delivery Address (including postcode): _____
_____
_____

Today's date: _____

Send to: Recipe Book Subscription Offer,
LighterLife, Cavendish House, Parkway, Harlow, Essex, CM19 5QF

*12 months subscription from the date entered on the above form.
For full terms and conditions, please see www.lighterlife.com/recipebookoffer